Practice Workbook

OKEMOS HIGH SCHOOL
MATHEMATICS DEPT.

#3

D1232679

GLENCOE
MATHEMATICS

Algebra 2

www.algebra2.com

Contents Include:
- 101 worksheets—one for each lesson

Glencoe
McGraw-Hill

New York, New York   Columbus, Ohio   Chicago, Illinois   Peoria, Illinois   Woodland Hills, California

To the Student:

This *Practice Workbook* gives you additional problems for the concept exercises in each lesson. The exercises are designed to aid your study of algebra by reinforcing important mathematical skills needed to succeed in the everyday world. The material is organized by chapter and lesson, with one practice worksheet for every lesson in *Glencoe Algebra 2*.

To the Teacher:

Answers to each worksheet are found in *Glencoe Algebra 2 Chapter Resource Masters* and also in the Teacher Wraparound Edition of *Glencoe Algebra 2*.

Glencoe/McGraw-Hill

A Division of The McGraw-Hill Companies

Send all inquiries to:
Glencoe/McGraw-Hill
8787 Orion Place
Columbus, OH 43240

ISBN: 0-07-828024-9

Algebra 2
Practice Workbook

3 4 5 6 7 009 08 07 06 05 04

Contents

1-1 Practice

Expressions and Formulas

Find the value of each expression.

1. $3(4 - 7) - 11$

2. $4(12 - 4^2)$

3. $1 + 2 - 3(4) \div 2$

4. $12 - [20 - 2(6^2 \div 3 \times 2^2)]$

5. $20 \div (5 - 3) + 5^2(3)$

6. $(-2)^3 - (3)(8) + (5)(10)$

7. $18 - \{5 - [34 - (17 - 11)]\}$

8. $[4(5 - 3) - 2(4 - 8)] \div 16$

9. $\frac{1}{2}[6 - 4^2]$

10. $\frac{1}{4}[-5 + 5(-3)]$

11. $\frac{-8(13 - 37)}{6}$

12. $\frac{(-8)^2}{5 - 9} - (-1)^2 + 4(-9)$

Evaluate each expression if $a = \frac{3}{4}$, $b = -8$, $c = -2$, $d = 3$, and $e = \frac{1}{3}$.

13. $ab^2 - d$

14. $(c + d)b$

15. $\frac{ab}{c} + d^2$

16. $\frac{d(b - c)}{ac}$

17. $(b - de)e^2$

18. $ac^3 - b^2de$

19. $-b[a + (c - d)^2]$

20. $\frac{ac^4}{d} - \frac{c}{e^2}$

21. $9bc - \frac{1}{e}$

22. $2ab^2 - (d^3 - c)$

23. TEMPERATURE The formula $F = \frac{9}{5}C + 32$ gives the temperature in degrees Fahrenheit for a given temperature in degrees Celsius. What is the temperature in degrees Fahrenheit when the temperature is -40 degrees Celsius?

24. PHYSICS The formula $h = 120t - 16t^2$ gives the height h in feet of an object t seconds after it is shot upward from Earth's surface with an initial velocity of 120 feet per second. What will the height of the object be after 6 seconds?

25. AGRICULTURE Faith owns an organic apple orchard. From her experience the last few seasons, she has developed the formula $P = 20x - 0.01x^2 - 240$ to predict her profit P in dollars this season if her trees produce x bushels of apples. What is Faith's predicted profit this season if her orchard produces 300 bushels of apples?

1-2 Practice

Properties of Real Numbers

Name the sets of numbers to which each number belongs.

1. 6425

2. $\sqrt{7}$

3. 2π

4. 0

5. $\sqrt{\dfrac{25}{36}}$

6. $-\sqrt{16}$

7. -35

8. -31.8

Name the property illustrated by each equation.

9. $5x \cdot (4y + 3x) = 5x \cdot (3x + 4y)$

10. $7x + (9x + 8) = (7x + 9x) + 8$

11. $5(3x + y) = 5(3x + 1y)$

12. $7n + 2n = (7 + 2)n$

13. $3(2x)y = (3 \cdot 2)(xy)$

14. $3x \cdot 2y = 3 \cdot 2 \cdot x \cdot y$

15. $(6 + -6)y = 0y$

16. $\dfrac{1}{4} \cdot 4y = 1y$

17. $5(x + y) = 5x + 5y$

18. $4n + 0 = 4n$

Name the additive inverse and multiplicative inverse for each number.

19. 0.4

20. -1.6

21. $-\dfrac{11}{16}$

22. $5\dfrac{5}{6}$

Simplify each expression.

23. $5x - 3y - 2x + 3y$

24. $-11a - 13b + 7a - 3b$

25. $8x - 7y - (3 - 6y)$

26. $4c - 2c - (4c + 2c)$

27. $3(r - 10s) - 4(7s + 2r)$

28. $\dfrac{1}{5}(10a - 15) + \dfrac{1}{2}(8 + 4a)$

29. $2(4 - 2x + y) - 4(5 + x - y)$

30. $\dfrac{5}{6}\left(\dfrac{3}{5}x + 12y\right) - \dfrac{1}{4}(2x - 12y)$

31. TRAVEL Olivia drives her car at 60 miles per hour for t hours. Ian drives his car at 50 miles per hour for $(t + 2)$ hours. Write a simplified expression for the sum of the distances traveled by the two cars.

32. NUMBER THEORY Use the properties of real numbers to tell whether the following statement is true or false: If $a > b$, it follows that $a\left(\dfrac{1}{a}\right) > b\left(\dfrac{1}{b}\right)$. Explain your reasoning.

1-3 Practice

Solving Equations

Write an algebraic expression to represent each verbal expression.

1. 2 more than the quotient of a number and 5

2. the sum of two consecutive integers

3. 5 times the sum of a number and 1

4. 1 less than twice the square of a number

Write a verbal expression to represent each equation.

5. $5 - 2x = 4$

6. $3y = 4y^3$

7. $3c = 2(c - 1)$

8. $\dfrac{m}{5} = 3(2m + 1)$

Name the property illustrated by each statement.

9. If $t - 13 = 52$, then $52 = t - 13$.

10. If $8(2q + 1) = 4$, then $2(2q + 1) = 1$.

11. If $h + 12 = 22$, then $h = 10$.

12. If $4m = -15$, then $-12m = 45$.

Solve each equation. Check your solution.

13. $14 = 8 - 6r$

14. $9 + 4n = -59$

15. $\dfrac{3}{4} - \dfrac{1}{2}n = \dfrac{5}{8}$

16. $\dfrac{5}{6}s + \dfrac{3}{4} = \dfrac{11}{12}$

17. $-1.6r + 5 = -7.8$

18. $6x - 5 = 7 - 9x$

19. $5(6 - 4v) = v + 21$

20. $6y - 5 = -3(2y + 1)$

Solve each equation or formula for the specified variable.

21. $E = mc^2$, for m

22. $c = \dfrac{2d + 1}{3}$, for d

23. $h = vt - gt^2$, for v

24. $E = \dfrac{1}{2}Iw^2 + U$, for I

Define a variable, write an equation, and solve the problem.

25. GEOMETRY The length of a rectangle is twice the width. Find the width if the perimeter is 60 centimeters.

26. GOLF Luis and three friends went golfing. Two of the friends rented clubs for $6 each. The total cost of the rented clubs and the green fees for each person was $76. What was the cost of the green fees for each person?

1-4 Practice

Solving Absolute Value Equations

Evaluate each expression if $a = -1$, $b = -8$, $c = 5$, and $d = -1.4$.

1. $|6a|$

2. $|2b + 4|$

3. $-|10d + a|$

4. $|17c| + |3b - 5|$

5. $-6|10a - 12|$

6. $|2b - 1| - |-8b + 5|$

7. $|5a - 7| + |3c - 4|$

8. $|1 - 7c| - |a|$

9. $-3|0.5c + 2| - |-0.5b|$

10. $|4d| + |5 - 2a|$

11. $|a - b| + |b - a|$

12. $|2 - 2d| - 3|b|$

Solve each equation. Check your solutions.

13. $|n - 4| = 13$

14. $|x - 13| = 2$

15. $|2y - 3| = 29$

16. $7|x + 3| = 42$

17. $|3u - 6| = 42$

18. $|5x - 4| = -6$

19. $-3|4x - 9| = 24$

20. $-6|5 - 2y| = -9$

21. $|8 + p| = 2p - 3$

22. $|4w - 1| = 5w + 37$

23. $4|2y - 7| + 5 = 9$

24. $-2|7 - 3y| - 6 = -14$

25. $2|4 - s| = -3s$

26. $5 - 3|2 + 2w| = -7$

27. $5|2r + 3| - 5 = 0$

28. $3 - 5|2d - 3| = 4$

29. **WEATHER** A thermometer comes with a guarantee that the stated temperature differs from the actual temperature by no more than 1.5 degrees Fahrenheit. Write and solve an equation to find the minimum and maximum actual temperatures when the thermometer states that the temperature is 87.4 degrees Fahrenheit.

30. **OPINION POLLS** Public opinion polls reported in newspapers are usually given with a margin of error. For example, a poll with a margin of error of ±5% is considered accurate to within plus or minus 5% of the actual value. A poll with a stated margin of error of ±3% predicts that candidate Tonwe will receive 51% of an upcoming vote. Write and solve an equation describing the minimum and maximum percent of the vote that candidate Tonwe is expected to receive.

1-5 Practice

Solving Inequalities

Solve each inequality. Describe the solution set using set-builder or interval notation. Then, graph the solution set on a number line.

1. $8x - 6 \geq 10$

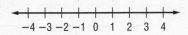
$$-4\ -3\ -2\ -1\ 0\ 1\ 2\ 3\ 4$$

2. $23 - 4u < 11$

$$-2\ -1\ 0\ 1\ 2\ 3\ 4\ 5\ 6$$

3. $-16 - 8r \geq 0$

$$-4\ -3\ -2\ -1\ 0\ 1\ 2\ 3\ 4$$

4. $14s < 9s + 5$

$$-4\ -3\ -2\ -1\ 0\ 1\ 2\ 3\ 4$$

5. $9x - 11 > 6x - 9$

$$-4\ -3\ -2\ -1\ 0\ 1\ 2\ 3\ 4$$

6. $-3(4w - 1) > 18$

$$-4\ -3\ -2\ -1\ 0\ 1\ 2\ 3\ 4$$

7. $1 - 8u \leq 3u - 10$

$$-4\ -3\ -2\ -1\ 0\ 1\ 2\ 3\ 4$$

8. $17.5 < 19 - 2.5x$

$$-4\ -3\ -2\ -1\ 0\ 1\ 2\ 3\ 4$$

9. $9(2r - 5) - 3 < 7r - 4$

10. $1 + 5(x - 8) \leq 2 - (x + 5)$

11. $\dfrac{4x - 3}{2} \geq -3.5$

12. $q - 2(2 - q) \leq 0$

13. $-36 - 2(w + 77) > -4(2w + 52)$

14. $4n - 5(n - 3) > 3(n + 1) - 4$

Define a variable and write an inequality for each problem. Then solve.

15. Twenty less than a number is more than twice the same number.

16. Four times the sum of twice a number and -3 is less than 5.5 times that same number.

17. HOTELS The Lincoln's hotel room costs $90 a night. An additional 10% tax is added. Hotel parking is $12 per day. The Lincoln's expect to spend $30 in tips during their stay. Solve the inequality $90x + 90(0.1)x + 12x + 30 \leq 600$ to find how many nights the Lincoln's can stay at the hotel without exceeding total hotel costs of $600.

18. BANKING Jan's account balance is $3800. Of this, $750 is for rent. Jan wants to keep a balance of at least $500. Write and solve an inequality describing how much she can withdraw and still meet these conditions.

1-6 Practice

Solving Compound and Absolute Value Inequalities

Write an absolute value inequality for each of the following. Then graph the solution set on a number line.

1. all numbers greater than 4 or less than −4

2. all numbers between −1.5 and 1.5, including −1.5 and 1.5

Write an absolute value inequality for each graph.

3.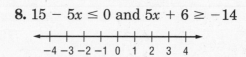

4.

Solve each inequality. Graph the solution set on a number line.

5. $-8 \leq 3y - 20 < 52$

6. $3(5x - 2) < 24$ or $6x - 4 > 4 + 5x$

7. $2x - 3 > 15$ or $3 - 7x < 17$

8. $15 - 5x \leq 0$ and $5x + 6 \geq -14$

9. $|2w| \geq 5$

10. $|y + 5| < 2$

11. $|x - 8| \geq 3$

12. $|2z - 2| \leq 3$

13. $|2x + 2| - 7 \leq -5$

14. $|x| > x - 1$

15. $|3b + 5| \leq -2$

16. $|3n - 2| - 2 < 1$

17. **RAINFALL** In 90% of the last 30 years, the rainfall at Shell Beach has varied no more than 6.5 inches from its mean value of 24 inches. Write and solve an absolute value inequality to describe the rainfall in the other 10% of the last 30 years.

18. **MANUFACTURING** A company's guidelines call for each can of soup produced not to vary from its stated volume of 14.5 fluid ounces by more than 0.08 ounces. Write and solve an absolute value inequality to describe acceptable can volumes.

2-1 Practice

Relations and Functions

Determine whether each relation is a function. Write *yes* or *no*.

1.

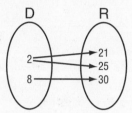

2.

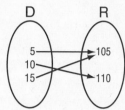

3.

x	y
−3	0
−1	−1
0	0
2	−2
3	4

4.

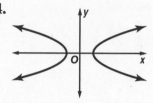

Graph each relation or equation and find the domain and range. Then determine whether the relation or equation is a function.

5. $\{(-4, -1), (4, 0), (0, 3), (2, 0)\}$

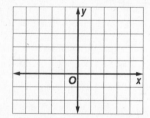

6. $y = 2x - 1$

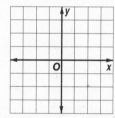

Find each value if $f(x) = \dfrac{5}{x + 2}$ and $g(x) = -2x + 3$.

7. $f(3)$

8. $f(-4)$

9. $g\left(\dfrac{1}{2}\right)$

10. $f(-2)$

11. $g(-6)$

12. $f(m - 2)$

13. MUSIC The ordered pairs (1, 16), (2, 16), (3, 32), (4, 32), and (5, 48) represent the cost of buying various numbers of CDs through a music club. Identify the domain and range of the relation. Is the relation a function?

14. COMPUTING If a computer can do one calculation in 0.0000000015 second, then the function $T(n) = 0.0000000015n$ gives the time required for the computer to do n calculations. How long would it take the computer to do 5 billion calculations?

2-2 # Practice

Linear Equations

State whether each equation or function is linear. Write *yes* or *no*. If no, explain your reasoning.

1. $h(x) = 23$

2. $y = \frac{2}{3}x$

3. $y = \frac{5}{x}$

4. $9 - 5xy = 2$

Write each equation in standard form. Identify *A*, *B*, and *C*.

5. $y = 7x - 5$

6. $y = \frac{3}{8}x + 5$

7. $3y - 5 = 0$

8. $x = -\frac{2}{7}y + \frac{3}{4}$

Find the *x*-intercept and the *y*-intercept of the graph of each equation. Then graph the equation.

9. $y = 2x + 4$

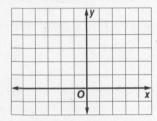

10. $2x + 7y = 14$

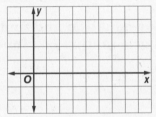

11. $y = -2x - 4$

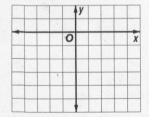

12. $6x + 2y = 6$

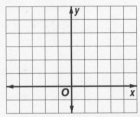

13. MEASURE The equation $y = 2.54x$ gives the length in centimeters corresponding to a length x in inches. What is the length in centimeters of a 1-foot ruler?

LONG DISTANCE For Exercises 14 and 15, use the following information.

For Meg's long-distance calling plan, the monthly cost C in dollars is given by the linear function $C(t) = 6 + 0.05t$, where t is the number of minutes talked.

14. What is the total cost of talking 8 hours? of talking 20 hours?

15. What is the effective cost per minute (the total cost divided by the number of minutes talked) of talking 8 hours? of talking 20 hours?

2-3 Practice

Slope

Find the slope of the line that passes through each pair of points.

1. $(3, -8), (-5, 2)$ **2.** $(-10, -3), (7, 2)$ **3.** $(-7, -6), (3, -6)$

4. $(8, 2), (8, -1)$ **5.** $(4, 3), (7, -2)$ **6.** $(-6, -3), (-8, 4)$

Graph the line passing through the given point with the given slope.

7. $(0, -3), m = 3$

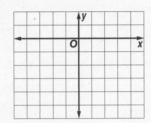

8. $(2, 1), m = -\dfrac{3}{4}$

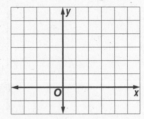

9. $(0, 2), m = 0$

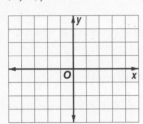

10. $(2, -3), m = \dfrac{4}{5}$

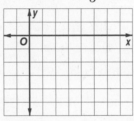

Graph the line that satisfies each set of conditions.

11. passes through $(3, 0)$, perpendicular to a line whose slope is $\dfrac{3}{2}$

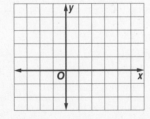

12. passes through $(-3, -1)$, parallel to a line whose slope is -1

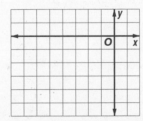

DEPRECIATION For Exercises 13–15, use the following information.

A machine that originally cost $15,600 has a value of $7500 at the end of 3 years. The same machine has a value of $2800 at the end of 8 years.

13. Find the average rate of change in value (depreciation) of the machine between its purchase and the end of 3 years.

14. Find the average rate of change in value of the machine between the end of 3 years and the end of 8 years.

15. Interpret the sign of your answers.

      9   *Glencoe Algebra 2*

2-4 Practice

Writing Linear Equations

State the slope and y-intercept of the graph of each equation.

1. $y = 8x + 12$
2. $y = 0.25x - 1$
3. $y = -\dfrac{3}{5}x$

4. $3y = 7$
5. $3x = -15 + 5y$
6. $2x - 3y = 10$

Write an equation in slope-intercept form for each graph.

7.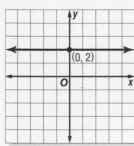

8.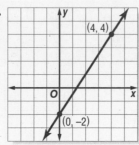

9.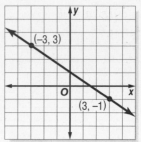

Write an equation in slope-intercept form for the line that satisfies each set of conditions.

10. slope -5, passes through $(-3, -8)$
11. slope $\dfrac{4}{5}$, passes through $(10, -3)$

12. slope 0, passes through $(0, -10)$
13. slope $-\dfrac{2}{3}$, passes through $(6, -8)$

14. passes through $(3, 11)$ and $(-6, 5)$
15. passes through $(7, -2)$ and $(3, -1)$

16. x-intercept 3, y-intercept 2
17. x-intercept -5, y-intercept 7

18. passes through $(-8, -7)$, perpendicular to the graph of $y = 4x - 3$

19. **RESERVOIRS** The surface of Grand Lake is at an elevation of 648 feet. During the current drought, the water level is dropping at a rate of 3 inches per day. If this trend continues, write an equation that gives the elevation in feet of the surface of Grand Lake after x days.

20. **BUSINESS** Tony Marconi's company manufactures CD-ROM drives. The company will make $150,000 profit if it manufactures 100,000 drives, and $1,750,000 profit if it manufactures 500,000 drives. The relationship between the number of drives manufactured and the profit is linear. Write an equation that gives the profit P when n drives are manufactured.

2-5 Practice

Modeling Real-World Data: Using Scatter Plots

For Exercises 1–3, complete parts a–c for each set of data.

a. Draw a scatter plot.

b. Use two ordered pairs to write a prediction equation.

c. Use your prediction equation to predict the missing value.

1. FUEL ECONOMY The table gives the approximate weights in tons and estimates for overall fuel economy in miles per gallon for several cars.

Weight (tons)	1.3	1.4	1.5	1.8	2	2.1	2.4
Miles per Gallon	29	24	23	21	?	17	15

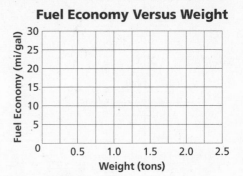

Fuel Economy Versus Weight

2. ALTITUDE In most cases, temperature decreases with increasing altitude. As Anchara drives into the mountains, her car thermometer registers the temperatures (°F) shown in the table at the given altitudes (feet).

Altitude (ft)	7500	8200	8600	9200	9700	10,400	12,000
Temperature (°F)	61	58	56	53	50	46	?

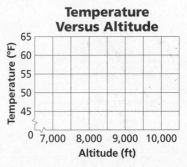

Temperature Versus Altitude

3. HEALTH Alton has a treadmill that uses the time on the treadmill and the speed of walking or running to estimate the number of Calories he burns during a workout. The table gives workout times and Calories burned for several workouts.

Time (min)	18	24	30	40	42	48	52	60
Calories Burned	260	280	320	380	400	440	475	?

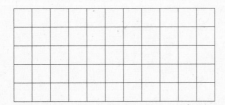

2-6 Practice

Special Functions

Graph each function. Identify the domain and range.

1. $f(x) = [\![0.5x]\!]$

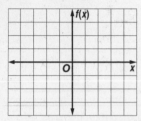

2. $f(x) = [\![x]\!] - 2$

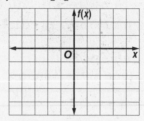

3. $g(x) = -2|x|$

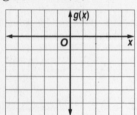

4. $f(x) = |x + 1|$

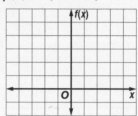

5. $f(x) = \begin{cases} x + 2 \text{ if } x \le -2 \\ 3x \text{ if } x > -2 \end{cases}$

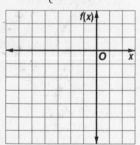

6. $h(x) = \begin{cases} 4 - x \text{ if } x > 0 \\ -2x - 2 \text{ if } x < 0 \end{cases}$

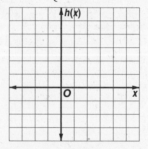

7. BUSINESS *A Stitch in Time* charges $40 per hour or any fraction thereof for labor. Draw a graph of the step function that represents this situation.

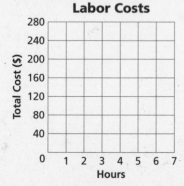

8. BUSINESS A wholesaler charges a store $3.00 per pound for less than 20 pounds of candy and $2.50 per pound for 20 or more pounds. Draw a graph of the function that represents this situation.

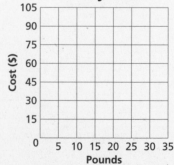

2-7 Practice

Graphing Inequalities

Graph each inequality.

1. $y \leq -3$

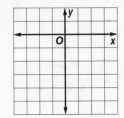

2. $x > 2$

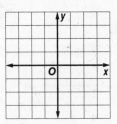

3. $x + y \leq -4$

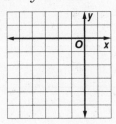

4. $y < -3x + 5$

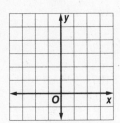

5. $y < \frac{1}{2}x + 3$

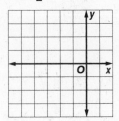

6. $y - 1 \geq -x$

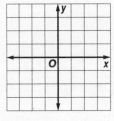

7. $x - 3y \leq 6$

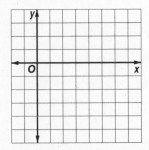

8. $y > |x| - 1$

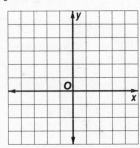

9. $y > -3|x + 1| - 2$

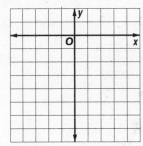

COMPUTERS For Exercises 10–12, use the following information.

A school system is buying new computers. They will buy desktop computers costing $1000 per unit, and notebook computers costing $1200 per unit. The total cost of the computers cannot exceed $80,000.

10. Write an inequality that describes this situation.

11. Graph the inequality.

12. If the school wants to buy 50 of the desktop computers and 25 of the notebook computers, will they have enough money?

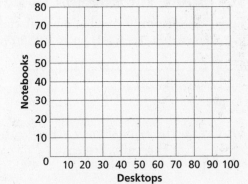

Glencoe Algebra 2

3-1 Practice

Solving Systems of Equations By Graphing

Solve each system of equations by graphing.

1. $x - 2y = 0$
$y = 2x - 3$

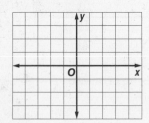

2. $x + 2y = 4$
$2x - 3y = 1$

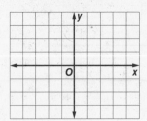

3. $2x + y = 3$
$y = \frac{1}{2}x - \frac{9}{2}$

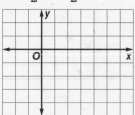

4. $y - x = 3$
$y = 1$

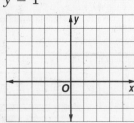

5. $2x - y = 6$
$x + 2y = -2$

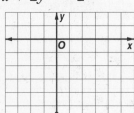

6. $5x - y = 4$
$-2x + 6y = 4$

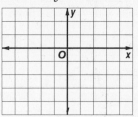

Graph each system of equations and describe it as *consistent and independent*, *consistent and dependent*, or *inconsistent*.

7. $2x - y = 4$
$x - y = 2$

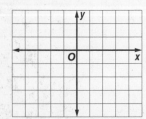

8. $y = -x - 2$
$x + y = -4$

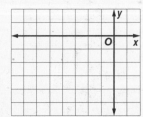

9. $2y - 8 = x$
$y = \frac{1}{2}x + 4$

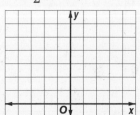

SOFTWARE **For Exercises 10–12, use the following information.**

Location Mapping needs new software. Software A costs $13,000 plus $500 per additional site license. Software B costs $2500 plus $1200 per additional site license.

10. Write two equations that represent the cost of each software.

11. Graph the equations. Estimate the break-even point of the software costs.

12. If Location Mapping plans to buy 10 additional site licenses, which software will cost less?

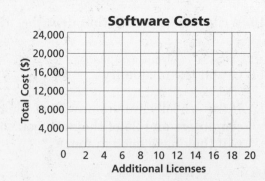

3-2 Practice

Solving Systems of Equations Algebraically

Solve each system of equations by using substitution.

1. $2x + y = 4$
   $3x + 2y = 1$

2. $x - 3y = 9$
   $x + 2y = -1$

3. $g + 3h = 8$
   $\frac{1}{3}g + h = 9$

4. $2a - 4b = 6$
   $-a + 2b = -3$

5. $2m + n = 6$
   $5m + 6n = 1$

6. $4x - 3y = -6$
   $-x - 2y = 7$

7. $u - 2v = \frac{1}{2}$
   $-u + 2v = 5$

8. $x - 3y = 16$
   $4x - y = 9$

9. $w + 3z = 1$
   $3w - 5z = -4$

Solve each system of equations by using elimination.

10. $2r + s = 5$
   $3r - s = 20$

11. $2m - n = -1$
   $3m + 2n = 30$

12. $6x + 3y = 6$
   $8x + 5y = 12$

13. $3j - k = 10$
   $4j - k = 16$

14. $2x - y = -4$
   $-4x + 2y = 6$

15. $2g + h = 6$
   $3g - 2h = 16$

16. $2t + 4v = 6$
   $-t - 2v = -3$

17. $3x - 2y = 12$
   $2x + \frac{2}{3}y = 14$

18. $\frac{1}{2}x + 3y = 11$
   $8x - 5y = 17$

Solve each system of equations by using either substitution or elimination.

19. $8x + 3y = -5$
   $10x + 6y = -13$

20. $8q - 15r = -40$
   $4q + 2r = 56$

21. $3x - 4y = 12$
   $\frac{1}{3}x - \frac{4}{9}y = \frac{4}{3}$

22. $4b - 2d = 5$
   $-2b + d = 1$

23. $s + 3y = 4$
   $s = 1$

24. $4m - 2p = 0$
   $-3m + 9p = 5$

25. $5g + 4k = 10$
   $-3g - 5k = 7$

26. $0.5x + 2y = 5$
   $x - 2y = -8$

27. $h - z = 3$
   $-3h + 3z = 6$

SPORTS For Exercises 28 and 29, use the following information.

Last year the volleyball team paid $5 per pair for socks and $17 per pair for shorts on a total purchase of $315. This year they spent $342 to buy the same number of pairs of socks and shorts because the socks now cost $6 a pair and the shorts cost $18.

28. Write a system of two equations that represents the number of pairs of socks and shorts bought each year.

29. How many pairs of socks and shorts did the team buy each year?

Glencoe Algebra 2

3-3 Practice

Solving Systems of Inequalities by Graphing

Solve each system of inequalities by graphing.

1. $y + 1 < -x$
$y \geq 1$

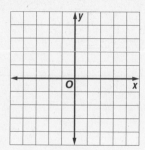

2. $x > -2$
$2y \geq 3x + 6$

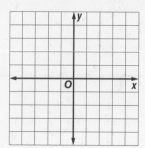

3. $y \leq 2x - 3$
$y \leq -\frac{1}{2}x + 2$

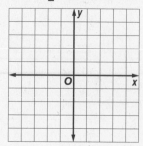

4. $x + y > -2$
$3x - y \geq -2$

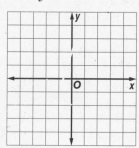

5. $|y| \leq 1$
$y < x - 1$

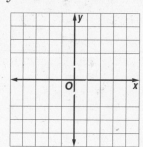

6. $3y > 4x$
$2x - 3y > -6$

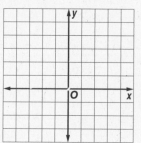

Find the coordinates of the vertices of the figure formed by each system of inequalities.

7. $y \geq 1 - x$
$y \leq x - 1$
$x \leq 3$

8. $x - y \leq 2$
$x + y \leq 2$
$x \geq -2$

9. $y \geq 2x - 2$
$2x + 3y \geq 6$
$y < 4$

DRAMA For Exercises 10 and 11, use the following information.

The drama club is selling tickets to its play. An adult ticket costs $15 and a student ticket costs $11. The auditorium will seat 300 ticket-holders. The drama club wants to collect at least $3630 from ticket sales.

10. Write and graph a system of four inequalities that describe how many of each type of ticket the club must sell to meets its goal.

11. List three different combinations of tickets sold that satisfy the inequalities.

3-4 Practice

Linear Programming

Graph each system of inequalities. Name the coordinates of the vertices of the feasible region. Find the maximum and minimum values of the given function for this region.

1. $2x - 4 \leq y$
$-2x - 4 \leq y$
$y \leq 2$
$f(x, y) = -2x + y$

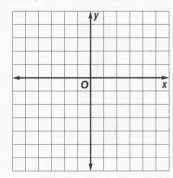

2. $3x - y \leq 7$
$2x - y \geq 3$
$y \geq x - 3$
$f(x, y) = x - 4y$

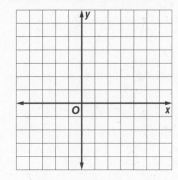

3. $x \geq 0$
$y \geq 0$
$y \leq 6$
$y \leq -3x + 15$
$f(x, y) = 3x + y$

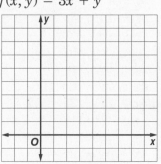

4. $x \leq 0$
$y \leq 0$
$4x + y \geq -7$
$f(x, y) = -x - 4y$

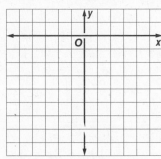

5. $y \leq 3x + 6$
$4y + 3x \leq 3$
$x \geq -2$
$f(x, y) = -x + 3y$

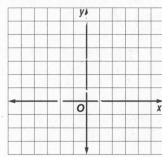

6. $2x + 3y \geq 6$
$2x - y \leq 2$
$x \geq 0$
$y \geq 0$
$f(x, y) = x + 4y + 3$

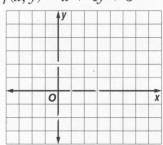

PRODUCTION For Exercises 7–9, use the following information.

A glass blower can form 8 simple vases or 2 elaborate vases in an hour. In a work shift of no more than 8 hours, the worker must form at least 40 vases.

7. Let *s* represent the hours forming simple vases and *e* the hours forming elaborate vases. Write a system of inequalities involving the time spent on each type of vase.

8. If the glass blower makes a profit of $30 per hour worked on the simple vases and $35 per hour worked on the elaborate vases, write a function for the total profit on the vases.

9. Find the number of hours the worker should spend on each type of vase to maximize profit. What is that profit?

3-5 Practice

Solving Systems of Equations in Three Variables

Solve each system of equations.

1. $2x - y + 2z = 15$
$-x + y + z = 3$
$3x - y + 2z = 18$

2. $x - 4y + 3z = -27$
$2x + 2y - 3z = 22$
$4z = -16$

3. $a + b = 3$
$-b + c = 3$
$a + 2c = 10$

4. $3m - 2n + 4p = 15$
$m - n + p = 3$
$m + 4n - 5p = 0$

5. $2g + 3h - 8j = 10$
$g - 4h = 1$
$-2g - 3h + 8j = 5$

6. $2x + y - z = -8$
$4x - y + 2z = -3$
$-3x + y + 2z = 5$

7. $2x - 5y + z = 5$
$3x + 2y - z = 17$
$4x - 3y + 2z = 17$

8. $2x + 3y + 4z = 2$
$5x - 2y + 3z = 0$
$x - 5y - 2z = -4$

9. $p + 4r = -7$
$p - 3q = -8$
$q + r = 1$

10. $4x + 4y - 2z = 8$
$3x - 5y + 3z = 0$
$2x + 2y - z = 4$

11. $d + 3e + f = 0$
$-d + 2e + f = -1$
$4d + e - f = 1$

12. $4x + y + 5z = -9$
$x - 4y - 2z = -2$
$2x + 3y - 2z = 21$

13. $5x + 9y + z = 20$
$2x - y - z = -21$
$5x + 2y + 2z = -21$

14. $2x + y - 3z = -3$
$3x + 2y + 4z = 5$
$-6x - 3y + 9z = 9$

15. $3x + 3y + z = 10$
$5x + 2y + 2z = 7$
$3x - 2y + 3z = -9$

16. $2u + v + w = 2$
$-3u + 2v + 3w = 7$
$-u - v + 2w = 7$

17. $x + 5y - 3z = -18$
$3x - 2y + 5z = 22$
$-2x - 3y + 8z = 28$

18. $x - 2y + z = -1$
$-x + 2y - z = 6$
$-4y + 2z = 1$

19. $2x - 2y - 4z = -2$
$3x - 3y - 6z = -3$
$-2x + 3y + z = 7$

20. $x - y + 9z = -27$
$2x - 4y - z = -1$
$3x + 6y - 3z = 27$

21. $2x - 5y - 3z = 7$
$-4x + 10y + 2z = 6$
$6x - 15y - z = -19$

22. The sum of three numbers is 6. The third number is the sum of the first and second numbers. The first number is one more than the third number. Find the numbers.

23. The sum of three numbers is -4. The second number decreased by the third is equal to the first. The sum of the first and second numbers is -5. Find the numbers.

24. SPORTS Alexandria High School scored 37 points in a football game. Six points are awarded for each touchdown. After each touchdown, the team can earn one point for the extra kick or two points for a 2-point conversion. The team scored one fewer 2-point conversions than extra kicks. The team scored 10 times during the game. How many touchdowns were made during the game?

4-1 Practice

Introduction to Matrices

State the dimensions of each matrix.

1. $[-3 \quad -3 \quad 7]$

2. $\begin{bmatrix} 5 & 8 & -1 \\ -2 & 1 & 8 \end{bmatrix}$

3. $\begin{bmatrix} -2 & 2 & -2 & 3 \\ 5 & 16 & 0 & 0 \\ 4 & 7 & -1 & 4 \end{bmatrix}$

Solve each equation.

4. $[4x \quad 42] = [24 \quad 6y]$

5. $[-2x \quad 22 \quad -3z] = [6x \quad -2y \quad 45]$

6. $\begin{bmatrix} 6x \\ 2y + 3 \end{bmatrix} = \begin{bmatrix} -36 \\ 17 \end{bmatrix}$

7. $\begin{bmatrix} 7x - 8 \\ 8y - 3 \end{bmatrix} = \begin{bmatrix} 20 \\ 2y + 3 \end{bmatrix}$

8. $\begin{bmatrix} -4x - 3 \\ 6y \end{bmatrix} = \begin{bmatrix} -3x \\ -2y + 16 \end{bmatrix}$

9. $\begin{bmatrix} 6x - 12 \\ -3y + 6 \end{bmatrix} = \begin{bmatrix} -3x - 21 \\ 8y - 5 \end{bmatrix}$

10. $\begin{bmatrix} -5 & 3x + 1 \\ 2y - 1 & 3z - 2 \end{bmatrix} = \begin{bmatrix} -5 & x - 1 \\ 3y & 5z - 4 \end{bmatrix}$

11. $\begin{bmatrix} 3x \\ y + 4 \end{bmatrix} = \begin{bmatrix} y + 8 \\ 17 \end{bmatrix}$

12. $\begin{bmatrix} 5x + 8y \\ 3x - 11 \end{bmatrix} = \begin{bmatrix} -1 \\ y \end{bmatrix}$

13. $\begin{bmatrix} 2x + y \\ 3x + 2y \end{bmatrix} = \begin{bmatrix} 0 \\ -2 \end{bmatrix}$

14. TICKET PRICES The table at the right gives ticket prices for a concert. Write a 2×3 matrix that represents the cost of a ticket.

	Child	Student	Adult
Cost Purchased in Advance	$6	$12	$18
Cost Purchased at the Door	$8	$15	$22

CONSTRUCTION For Exercises 15 and 16, use the following information.

During each of the last three weeks, a road-building crew has used three truck-loads of gravel. The table at the right shows the amount of gravel in each load.

Week 1	Week 2	Week 3
Load 1 40 tons	Load 1 40 tons	Load 1 32 tons
Load 2 32 tons	Load 2 40 tons	Load 2 24 tons
Load 3 24 tons	Load 3 32 tons	Load 3 24 tons

15. Write a matrix for the amount of gravel in each load.

16. What are the dimensions of the matrix?

4-2 Practice

Operations with Matrices

Perform the indicated matrix operations. If the matrix does not exist, write *impossible*.

1. $\begin{bmatrix} 2 & -1 \\ 3 & 7 \\ 14 & -9 \end{bmatrix} + \begin{bmatrix} -6 & 9 \\ 7 & -11 \\ -8 & 17 \end{bmatrix}$

2. $\begin{bmatrix} 4 \\ -71 \\ 18 \end{bmatrix} - \begin{bmatrix} -67 \\ 45 \\ -24 \end{bmatrix}$

3. $-3\begin{bmatrix} -1 & 0 \\ 17 & -11 \end{bmatrix} + 4\begin{bmatrix} -3 & 16 \\ -21 & 12 \end{bmatrix}$

4. $7\begin{bmatrix} 2 & -1 & 8 \\ 4 & 7 & 9 \end{bmatrix} - 2\begin{bmatrix} -1 & 4 & -3 \\ 7 & 2 & -6 \end{bmatrix}$

5. $-2\begin{bmatrix} 1 \\ 2 \end{bmatrix} + 4\begin{bmatrix} 0 \\ 5 \end{bmatrix} - \begin{bmatrix} 10 \\ 18 \end{bmatrix}$

6. $\frac{3}{4}\begin{bmatrix} 8 & 12 \\ -16 & 20 \end{bmatrix} + \frac{2}{3}\begin{bmatrix} 27 & -9 \\ 54 & -18 \end{bmatrix}$

Use $A = \begin{bmatrix} 4 & -1 & 0 \\ -3 & 6 & 2 \end{bmatrix}$, $B = \begin{bmatrix} -2 & 4 & 5 \\ 1 & 0 & -9 \end{bmatrix}$, and $C = \begin{bmatrix} 10 & -8 & 6 \\ -6 & -4 & 20 \end{bmatrix}$ to find the following.

7. $A - B$

8. $A - C$

9. $-3B$

10. $4B - A$

11. $-2B - 3C$

12. $A + 0.5C$

ECONOMICS For Exercises 13 and 14, use the table that shows loans by an economic development board to women and men starting new businesses.

	Women		Men	
	Businesses	Loan Amount ($)	Businesses	Loan Amount ($)
1999	27	$567,000	36	$864,000
2000	41	$902,000	32	$672,000
2001	35	$777,000	28	$562,000

13. Write two matrices that represent the number of new businesses and loan amounts, one for women and one for men.

14. Find the sum of the numbers of new businesses and loan amounts for both men and women over the three-year period expressed as a matrix.

15. **PET NUTRITION** Use the table that gives nutritional information for two types of dog food. Find the difference in the percent of protein, fat, and fiber between Mix B and Mix A expressed as a matrix.

	% Protein	% Fat	% Fiber
Mix A	22	12	5
Mix B	24	8	8

4-3 Practice

Multiplying Matrices

Determine whether each matrix product is defined. If so, state the dimensions of the product.

1. $A_{7 \times 4} \cdot B_{4 \times 3}$ **2.** $A_{3 \times 5} \cdot M_{5 \times 8}$ **3.** $M_{2 \times 1} \cdot A_{1 \times 6}$

4. $M_{3 \times 2} \cdot A_{3 \times 2}$ **5.** $P_{1 \times 9} \cdot Q_{9 \times 1}$ **6.** $P_{9 \times 1} \cdot Q_{1 \times 9}$

Find each product, if possible.

7. $\begin{bmatrix} 2 & 4 \\ 3 & -1 \end{bmatrix} \cdot \begin{bmatrix} 3 & -2 & 7 \\ 6 & 0 & -5 \end{bmatrix}$ **8.** $\begin{bmatrix} 2 & 4 \\ 7 & -1 \end{bmatrix} \cdot \begin{bmatrix} -3 & 0 \\ 2 & 5 \end{bmatrix}$

9. $\begin{bmatrix} -3 & 0 \\ 2 & 5 \end{bmatrix} \cdot \begin{bmatrix} 2 & 4 \\ 7 & -1 \end{bmatrix}$ **10.** $\begin{bmatrix} 3 & -2 & 7 \\ 6 & 0 & -5 \end{bmatrix} \cdot \begin{bmatrix} 3 & -2 & 7 \\ 6 & 0 & -5 \end{bmatrix}$

11. $[4 \quad 0 \quad 2] \cdot \begin{bmatrix} 1 \\ 3 \\ -1 \end{bmatrix}$ **12.** $\begin{bmatrix} 1 \\ 3 \\ -1 \end{bmatrix} \cdot [4 \quad 0 \quad 2]$

13. $\begin{bmatrix} -6 & 2 \\ 3 & -1 \end{bmatrix} \cdot \begin{bmatrix} 5 & 0 \\ 0 & 5 \end{bmatrix}$ **14.** $[-15 \quad -9] \cdot \begin{bmatrix} 6 & 11 \\ 23 & -10 \end{bmatrix}$

Use $A = \begin{bmatrix} 1 & 3 \\ 3 & 1 \end{bmatrix}$, $B = \begin{bmatrix} 4 & 0 \\ -2 & -1 \end{bmatrix}$, $C = \begin{bmatrix} -1 & 0 \\ 0 & -1 \end{bmatrix}$, and scalar $c = 3$ to determine whether the following equations are true for the given matrices.

15. $AC = CA$ **16.** $A(B + C) = BA + CA$

17. $(AB)c = c(AB)$ **18.** $(A + C)B = B(A + C)$

RENTALS For Exercises 19–21, use the following information.

For their one-week vacation, the Montoyas can rent a 2-bedroom condominium for $1796, a 3-bedroom condominium for $2165, or a 4-bedroom condominium for $2538. The table shows the number of units in each of three complexes.

	2-Bedroom	3-Bedroom	4-Bedroom
Sun Haven	36	24	22
Surfside	29	32	42
Seabreeze	18	22	18

19. Write a matrix that represents the number of each type of unit available at each complex and a matrix that represents the weekly charge for each type of unit.

20. If all of the units in the three complexes are rented for the week at the rates given the Montoyas, express the income of each of the three complexes as a matrix.

21. What is the total income of all three complexes for the week?

4-4 Practice

Transformations with Matrices

For Exercises 1–3, use the following information.

Quadrilateral $WXYZ$ with vertices $W(-3, 2)$, $X(-2, 4)$, $Y(4, 1)$, and $Z(3, 0)$ is translated 1 unit left and 3 units down.

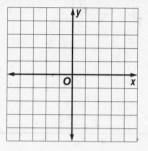

1. Write the translation matrix.

2. Find the coordinates of quadrilateral $W'X'Y'Z'$.

3. Graph the preimage and the image.

For Exercises 4–6, use the following information.

The vertices of $\triangle RST$ are $R(6, 2)$, $S(3, -3)$, and $T(-2, 5)$. The triangle is dilated so that its perimeter is one half the original perimeter.

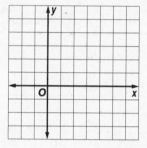

4. Write the coordinates of $\triangle RST$ in a vertex matrix.

5. Find the coordinates of the image $\triangle R'S'T'$.

6. Graph $\triangle RST$ and $\triangle R'S'T'$.

For Exercises 7–10, use the following information.

The vertices of quadrilateral $ABCD$ are $A(-3, 2)$, $B(0, 3)$, $C(4, -4)$, and $D(-2, -2)$. The quadrilateral is reflected over the y-axis.

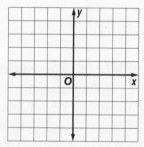

7. Write the coordinates of $ABCD$ in a vertex matrix.

8. Write the reflection matrix for this situation.

9. Find the coordinates of $A'B'C'D'$.

10. Graph $ABCD$ and $A'B'C'D'$.

11. **ARCHITECTURE** Using architectural design software, the Bradleys plot their kitchen plans on a grid with each unit representing 1 foot. They place the corners of an island at $(2, 8)$, $(8, 11)$, $(3, 5)$, and $(9, 8)$. If the Bradleys wish to move the island 1.5 feet to the right and 2 feet down, what will the new coordinates of its corners be?

12. **BUSINESS** The design of a business logo calls for locating the vertices of a triangle at $(1.5, 5)$, $(4, 1)$, and $(1, 0)$ on a grid. If design changes require rotating the triangle 90° counterclockwise, what will the new coordinates of the vertices be?

4-5 Practice

Determinants

Find the value of each determinant.

1. $\begin{vmatrix} 1 & 6 \\ 2 & 7 \end{vmatrix}$

2. $\begin{vmatrix} 9 & 6 \\ 3 & 2 \end{vmatrix}$

3. $\begin{vmatrix} 4 & 1 \\ -2 & -5 \end{vmatrix}$

4. $\begin{vmatrix} -14 & -3 \\ 2 & -2 \end{vmatrix}$

5. $\begin{vmatrix} 4 & -3 \\ -12 & 4 \end{vmatrix}$

6. $\begin{vmatrix} 2 & -5 \\ 5 & -11 \end{vmatrix}$

7. $\begin{vmatrix} 4 & 0 \\ -2 & 9 \end{vmatrix}$

8. $\begin{vmatrix} 3 & -4 \\ 7 & 9 \end{vmatrix}$

9. $\begin{vmatrix} -1 & -11 \\ 10 & -2 \end{vmatrix}$

10. $\begin{vmatrix} 3 & -4 \\ 3.75 & 5 \end{vmatrix}$

11. $\begin{vmatrix} 2 & -1 \\ 3 & -9.5 \end{vmatrix}$

12. $\begin{vmatrix} 0.5 & -0.7 \\ 0.4 & -0.3 \end{vmatrix}$

Evaluate each determinant using expansion by minors.

13. $\begin{vmatrix} -2 & 3 & 1 \\ 0 & 4 & -3 \\ 2 & 5 & -1 \end{vmatrix}$

14. $\begin{vmatrix} 2 & -4 & 1 \\ 3 & 0 & 9 \\ -1 & 5 & 7 \end{vmatrix}$

15. $\begin{vmatrix} 2 & 1 & 1 \\ 1 & -1 & -2 \\ 1 & 1 & -1 \end{vmatrix}$

16. $\begin{vmatrix} 0 & -4 & 0 \\ 2 & -1 & 1 \\ 3 & -2 & 5 \end{vmatrix}$

17. $\begin{vmatrix} 2 & 7 & -6 \\ 8 & 4 & 0 \\ 1 & -1 & 3 \end{vmatrix}$

18. $\begin{vmatrix} -12 & 0 & 3 \\ 7 & 5 & -1 \\ 4 & 2 & -6 \end{vmatrix}$

Evaluate each determinant using diagonals.

19. $\begin{vmatrix} -4 & 3 & -1 \\ 2 & 1 & -2 \\ 4 & 1 & -4 \end{vmatrix}$

20. $\begin{vmatrix} 2 & 2 & 3 \\ 1 & -1 & 1 \\ 3 & 1 & 1 \end{vmatrix}$

21. $\begin{vmatrix} 1 & -4 & -1 \\ 1 & -6 & -2 \\ 2 & 3 & 1 \end{vmatrix}$

22. $\begin{vmatrix} 1 & 2 & -4 \\ 1 & 4 & -6 \\ 2 & 3 & 3 \end{vmatrix}$

23. $\begin{vmatrix} 2 & -1 & -2 \\ 4 & 0 & -2 \\ 0 & 3 & 2 \end{vmatrix}$

24. $\begin{vmatrix} 2 & 1 & 3 \\ 1 & 8 & 0 \\ 0 & 5 & -1 \end{vmatrix}$

25. **GEOMETRY** Find the area of a triangle whose vertices have coordinates $(3, 5)$, $(6, -5)$, and $(-4, 10)$.

26. **LAND MANAGEMENT** A fish and wildlife management organization uses a GIS (geographic information system) to store and analyze data for the parcels of land it manages. All of the parcels are mapped on a grid in which 1 unit represents 1 acre. If the coordinates of the corners of a parcel are $(-8, 10)$, $(6, 17)$, and $(2, -4)$, how many acres is the parcel?

4-6 Practice

Cramer's Rule

Use Cramer's Rule to solve each system of equations.

1. $2x + y = 0$
$3x + 2y = -2$

2. $5c + 9d = 19$
$2c - d = -20$

3. $2x + 3y = 5$
$3x - 2y = 1$

4. $20m - 3n = 28$
$2m + 3n = 16$

5. $x - 3y = 6$
$3x + y = -22$

6. $5x - 6y = -45$
$9x + 8y = 13$

7. $-2e + f = 4$
$-3e + 5f = -15$

8. $2x - y = -1$
$2x - 4y = 8$

9. $8a + 3b = 24$
$2a + b = 4$

10. $-3x + 15y = 45$
$-2x + 7y = 18$

11. $3u - 5v = 11$
$6u + 7v = -12$

12. $-6g + h = -10$
$-3g - 4h = 4$

13. $x - 3y = 8$
$x - 0.5y = 3$

14. $0.2x - 0.5y = -1$
$0.6x - 3y = -9$

15. $0.3d - 0.6g = 1.8$
$0.2d + 0.3g = 0.5$

16. GEOMETRY The two sides of an angle are contained in the lines whose equations are $x - \frac{4}{3}y = 6$ and $2x + y = 1$. Find the coordinates of the vertex of the angle.

17. GEOMETRY Two sides of a parallelogram are contained in the lines whose equations are $0.2x - 0.5y = 1$ and $0.02x - 0.3y = -0.9$. Find the coordinates of a vertex of the parallelogram.

Use Cramer's Rule to solve each system of equations.

18. $x + 3y + 3z = 4$
$-x + 2y + z = -1$
$4x + y - 2z = -1$

19. $-5a + b - 4c = 7$
$-3a + 2b - c = 0$
$2a + 3b - c = 17$

20. $2x + y - 3z = -5$
$5x + 2y - 2z = 8$
$3x - 3y + 5z = 17$

21. $2c + 3d - e = 17$
$4c + d + 5e = -9$
$c + 2d - e = 12$

22. $2j + k - 3m = -3$
$3j + 2k + 4m = 5$
$-4j - k + 2m = 4$

23. $3x - 2y + 5z = 3$
$2x + 2y - 4z = 3$
$-5x + 10y + 7z = -3$

24. LANDSCAPING A memorial garden being planted in front of a municipal library will contain three circular beds that are tangent to each other. A landscape architect has prepared a sketch of the design for the garden using CAD (computer-aided drafting) software, as shown at the right. The centers of the three circular beds are represented by points A, B, and C. The distance from A to B is 15 feet, the distance from B to C is 13 feet, and the distance from A to C is 16 feet. What is the radius of each of the circular beds?

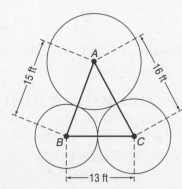

4-7 Practice

Identity and Inverse Matrices

Determine whether each pair of matrices are inverses.

1. $M = \begin{bmatrix} 2 & 1 \\ 3 & 2 \end{bmatrix}$, $N = \begin{bmatrix} -2 & 1 \\ 3 & -2 \end{bmatrix}$

2. $X = \begin{bmatrix} -3 & 2 \\ 5 & -3 \end{bmatrix}$, $Y = \begin{bmatrix} 3 & 2 \\ 5 & 3 \end{bmatrix}$

3. $A = \begin{bmatrix} 3 & 1 \\ -4 & 2 \end{bmatrix}$, $B = \begin{bmatrix} \frac{1}{5} & -\frac{1}{10} \\ \frac{2}{5} & \frac{3}{10} \end{bmatrix}$

4. $P = \begin{bmatrix} 6 & -2 \\ -2 & 3 \end{bmatrix}$, $Q = \begin{bmatrix} \frac{3}{14} & \frac{1}{7} \\ \frac{1}{7} & \frac{3}{7} \end{bmatrix}$

Determine whether each statement is *true* or *false*.

5. All square matrices have multiplicative inverses.

6. All square matrices have multiplicative identities.

Find the inverse of each matrix, if it exists.

7. $\begin{bmatrix} 4 & 5 \\ -4 & -3 \end{bmatrix}$

8. $\begin{bmatrix} 2 & 0 \\ 3 & 5 \end{bmatrix}$

9. $\begin{bmatrix} -1 & 3 \\ 4 & -7 \end{bmatrix}$

10. $\begin{bmatrix} 2 & 5 \\ -1 & 3 \end{bmatrix}$

11. $\begin{bmatrix} 2 & -5 \\ 3 & 1 \end{bmatrix}$

12. $\begin{bmatrix} 4 & 6 \\ 6 & 9 \end{bmatrix}$

GEOMETRY For Exercises 13–16, use the figure at the right.

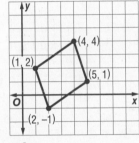

13. Write the vertex matrix A for the rectangle.

14. Use matrix multiplication to find BA if $B = \begin{bmatrix} 1.5 & 0 \\ 0 & 1.5 \end{bmatrix}$.

15. Graph the vertices of the transformed rectangle on the previous graph. Describe the transformation.

16. Make a conjecture about what transformation B^{-1} describes on a coordinate plane.

17. CODES Use the alphabet table below and the inverse of coding matrix $C = \begin{bmatrix} 1 & 2 \\ 2 & 1 \end{bmatrix}$ to decode this message:

19 | 14 | 11 | 13 | 11 | 22 | 55 | 65 | 57 | 60 | 2 | 1 | 52 | 47 | 33 | 51 | 56 | 55.

CODE													
A	1	B	2	C	3	D	4	E	5	F	6	G	7
H	8	I	9	J	10	K	11	L	12	M	13	N	14
O	15	P	16	Q	17	R	18	S	19	T	20	U	21
V	22	W	23	X	24	Y	25	Z	26	–	0		

4-8 Practice

Using Matrices to Solve Systems of Equations

Write a matrix equation for each system of equations.

1. $-3x + 2y = 9$
$5x - 3y = -13$

2. $6x - 2y = -2$
$3x + 3y = 10$

3. $2a + b = 0$
$3a + 2b = -2$

4. $r + 5s = 10$
$2r - 3s = 7$

5. $3x - 2y + 5z = 3$
$x + y - 4z = 2$
$-2x + 2y + 7z = -5$

6. $2m + n - 3p = -5$
$5m + 2n - 2p = 8$
$3m - 3n + 5p = 17$

Solve each matrix equation or system of equations by using inverse matrices.

7. $\begin{bmatrix} 2 & 1 \\ 3 & 2 \end{bmatrix} \cdot \begin{bmatrix} g \\ h \end{bmatrix} = \begin{bmatrix} 0 \\ -2 \end{bmatrix}$

8. $\begin{bmatrix} -2 & 3 \\ 1 & 5 \end{bmatrix} \cdot \begin{bmatrix} x \\ y \end{bmatrix} = \begin{bmatrix} -7 \\ 10 \end{bmatrix}$

9. $\begin{bmatrix} -1 & -3 \\ 3 & 4 \end{bmatrix} \cdot \begin{bmatrix} a \\ b \end{bmatrix} = \begin{bmatrix} 12 \\ -11 \end{bmatrix}$

10. $\begin{bmatrix} -5 & 3 \\ 6 & 4 \end{bmatrix} \cdot \begin{bmatrix} c \\ d \end{bmatrix} = \begin{bmatrix} 16 \\ 34 \end{bmatrix}$

11. $\begin{bmatrix} -4 & 2 \\ 7 & 4 \end{bmatrix} \cdot \begin{bmatrix} r \\ s \end{bmatrix} = \begin{bmatrix} 17 \\ -26 \end{bmatrix}$

12. $\begin{bmatrix} 8 & 3 \\ 12 & 6 \end{bmatrix} \cdot \begin{bmatrix} y \\ z \end{bmatrix} = \begin{bmatrix} -1 \\ -1 \end{bmatrix}$

13. $2x + 3y = 5$
$3x - 2y = 1$

14. $8d + 9f = 13$
$-6d + 5f = -45$

15. $5m + 9n = 19$
$2m - n = -20$

16. $-4j + 9k = -8$
$6j + 12k = -5$

17. AIRLINE TICKETS Last Monday at 7:30 A.M., an airline flew 89 passengers on a commuter flight from Boston to New York. Some of the passengers paid $120 for their tickets and the rest paid $230 for their tickets. The total cost of all of the tickets was $14,200. How many passengers bought $120 tickets? How many bought $230 tickets?

18. NUTRITION A single dose of a dietary supplement contains 0.2 gram of calcium and 0.2 gram of vitamin C. A single dose of a second dietary supplement contains 0.1 gram of calcium and 0.4 gram of vitamin C. If a person wants to take 0.6 gram of calcium and 1.2 grams of vitamin C, how many doses of each supplement should she take?

5-1 Practice

Monomials

Simplify. Assume that no variable equals 0.

1. $n^5 \cdot n^2$

2. $y^7 \cdot y^3 \cdot y^2$

3. $t^9 \cdot t^{-8}$

4. $x^{-4} \cdot x^{-4} \cdot x^4$

5. $(2f^4)^6$

6. $(-2b^{-2}c^3)^3$

7. $(4d^2t^5v^{-4})(-5dt^{-3}v^{-1})$

8. $8u(2z)^3$

9. $\dfrac{12m^8y^6}{-9my^4}$

10. $\dfrac{-6s^5x^3}{18sx^7}$

11. $\dfrac{-27x^3(-x^7)}{16x^4}$

12. $\left(\dfrac{2}{3r^2s^3z^6}\right)^2$

13. $-(4w^{-3}z^{-5})(8w)^2$

14. $(m^4n^6)^4(m^3n^2p^5)^6$

15. $\left(\dfrac{3}{2}d^2f^4\right)^4\left(-\dfrac{4}{3}d^5f\right)^3$

16. $\left(\dfrac{2x^3y^2}{-x^2y^5}\right)^{-2}$

17. $\dfrac{(3x^{-2}y^3)(5xy^{-8})}{(x^{-3})^4y^{-2}}$

18. $\dfrac{-20(m^2v)(-v)^3}{5(-v)^2(-m^4)}$

Express each number in scientific notation.

19. 896,000

20. 0.000056

21. 433.7×10^8

Evaluate. Express the result in scientific notation.

22. $(4.8 \times 10^2)(6.9 \times 10^4)$

23. $(3.7 \times 10^9)(8.7 \times 10^2)$

24. $\dfrac{2.7 \times 10^6}{9 \times 10^{10}}$

25. COMPUTING The term *bit*, short for *binary digit*, was first used in 1946 by John Tukey. A single bit holds a zero or a one. Some computers use 32-bit numbers, or strings of 32 consecutive bits, to identify each address in their memories. Each 32-bit number corresponds to a number in our base-ten system. The largest 32-bit number is nearly 4,295,000,000. Write this number in scientific notation.

26. LIGHT When light passes through water, its velocity is reduced by 25%. If the speed of light in a vacuum is 1.86×10^5 miles per second, at what velocity does it travel through water? Write your answer in scientific notation.

27. TREES Deciduous and coniferous trees are hard to distinguish in a black-and-white photo. But because deciduous trees reflect infrared energy better than coniferous trees, the two types of trees are more distinguishable in an infrared photo. If an infrared wavelength measures about 8×10^{-7} meters and a blue wavelength measures about 4.5×10^{-7} meters, about how many times longer is the infrared wavelength than the blue wavelength?

5-2 Practice

Polynomials

Determine whether each expression is a polynomial. If it is a polynomial, state the degree of the polynomial.

1. $5x^3 + 2xy^4 + 6xy$

2. $-\dfrac{4}{3}ac - a^5d^3$

3. $\dfrac{12m^8n^9}{(m-n)^2}$

4. $25x^3z - x\sqrt{78}$

5. $6c^{-2} + c - 1$

6. $\dfrac{5}{r} + \dfrac{6}{s}$

Simplify.

7. $(3n^2 + 1) + (8n^2 - 8)$

8. $(6w - 11w^2) - (4 + 7w^2)$

9. $(-6n - 13n^2) + (-3n + 9n^2)$

10. $(8x^2 - 3x) - (4x^2 + 5x - 3)$

11. $(5m^2 - 2mp - 6p^2) - (-3m^2 + 5mp + p^2)$

12. $(2x^2 - xy + y^2) + (-3x^2 + 4xy + 3y^2)$

13. $(5t - 7) + (2t^2 + 3t + 12)$

14. $(u - 4) - (6 + 3u^2 - 4u)$

15. $-9(y^2 - 7w)$

16. $-9r^4y^2(-3ry^7 + 2r^3y^4 - 8r^{10})$

17. $-6a^2w(a^3w - aw^4)$

18. $5a^2w^3(a^2w^6 - 3a^4w^2 + 9aw^6)$

19. $2x^2(x^2 + xy - 2y^2)$

20. $-\dfrac{3}{5}ab^3d^2(-5ab^2d^5 - 5ab)$

21. $(v^2 - 6)(v^2 + 4)$

22. $(7a + 9y)(2a - y)$

23. $(y - 8)^2$

24. $(x^2 + 5y)^2$

25. $(5x + 4w)(5x - 4w)$

26. $(2n^4 - 3)(2n^4 + 3)$

27. $(w + 2s)(w^2 - 2ws + 4s^2)$

28. $(x + y)(x^2 - 3xy + 2y^2)$

29. BANKING Terry invests $1500 in two mutual funds. The first year, one fund grows 3.8% and the other grows 6%. Write a polynomial to represent the amount Terry's $1500 grows to in that year if x represents the amount he invested in the fund with the lesser growth rate.

30. GEOMETRY The area of the base of a rectangular box measures $2x^2 + 4x - 3$ square units. The height of the box measures x units. Find a polynomial expression for the volume of the box.

5-3 Practice

Dividing Polynomials

Simplify.

1. $\dfrac{15r^{10} - 5r^8 + 40r^2}{5r^4}$

2. $\dfrac{6k^2m - 12k^3m^2 + 9m^3}{2km^2}$

3. $(-30x^3y + 12x^2y^2 - 18x^2y) \div (-6x^2y)$

4. $(-6w^3z^4 - 3w^2z^5 + 4w + 5z) \div (2w^2z)$

5. $(4a^3 - 8a^2 + a^2)(4a)^{-1}$

6. $(28d^3k^2 + d^2k^2 - 4dk^2)(4dk^2)^{-1}$

7. $\dfrac{f^2 + 7f + 10}{f + 2}$

8. $\dfrac{2x^2 + 3x - 14}{x - 2}$

9. $(a^3 - 64) \div (a - 4)$

10. $(b^3 + 27) \div (b + 3)$

11. $\dfrac{2x^3 + 6x + 152}{x + 4}$

12. $\dfrac{2x^3 + 4x - 6}{x + 3}$

13. $(3w^3 + 7w^2 - 4w + 3) \div (w + 3)$

14. $(6y^4 + 15y^3 - 28y - 6) \div (y + 2)$

15. $(x^4 - 3x^3 - 11x^2 + 3x + 10) \div (x - 5)$

16. $(3m^5 + m - 1) \div (m + 1)$

17. $(x^4 - 3x^3 + 5x - 6)(x + 2)^{-1}$

18. $(6y^2 - 5y - 15)(2y + 3)^{-1}$

19. $\dfrac{4x^2 - 2x + 6}{2x - 3}$

20. $\dfrac{6x^2 - x - 7}{3x + 1}$

21. $(2r^3 + 5r^2 - 2r - 15) \div (2r - 3)$

22. $(6t^3 + 5t^2 - 2t + 1) \div (3t + 1)$

23. $\dfrac{4p^4 - 17p^2 + 14p - 3}{2p - 3}$

24. $\dfrac{2h^4 - h^3 + h^2 + h - 3}{h^2 - 1}$

25. **GEOMETRY** The area of a rectangle is $2x^2 - 11x + 15$ square feet. The length of the rectangle is $2x - 5$ feet. What is the width of the rectangle?

26. **GEOMETRY** The area of a triangle is $15x^4 + 3x^3 + 4x^2 - x - 3$ square meters. The length of the base of the triangle is $6x^2 - 2$ meters. What is the height of the triangle?

5-4 Practice

Factoring Polynomials

Factor completely. If the polynomial is not factorable, write *prime*.

1. $15a^2b - 10ab^2$

2. $3st^2 - 9s^3t + 6s^2t^2$

3. $3x^3y^2 - 2x^2y + 5xy$

4. $2x^3y - x^2y + 5xy^2 + xy^3$

5. $21 - 7t + 3r - rt$

6. $x^2 - xy + 2x - 2y$

7. $y^2 + 20y + 96$

8. $4ab + 2a + 6b + 3$

9. $6n^2 - 11n - 2$

10. $6x^2 + 7x - 3$

11. $x^2 - 8x - 8$

12. $6p^2 - 17p - 45$

13. $r^3 + 3r^2 - 54r$

14. $8a^2 + 2a - 6$

15. $c^2 - 49$

16. $x^3 + 8$

17. $16r^2 - 169$

18. $b^4 - 81$

19. $8m^3 - 25$

20. $2t^3 + 32t^2 + 128t$

21. $5y^5 + 135y^2$

22. $81x^4 - 16$

Simplify. Assume that no denominator is equal to 0.

23. $\dfrac{x^2 - 16}{x^2 + x - 20}$

24. $\dfrac{x^2 - 16x + 64}{x^2 + x - 72}$

25. $\dfrac{3x^2 - 27}{x^3 - 27}$

26. DESIGN Bobbi Jo is using a software package to create a drawing of a cross section of a brace as shown at the right. Write a simplified, factored expression that represents the area of the cross section of the brace.

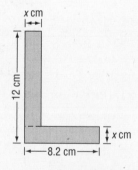

27. COMBUSTION ENGINES In an internal combustion engine, the up and down motion of the pistons is converted into the rotary motion of the crankshaft, which drives the flywheel. Let r_1 represent the radius of the flywheel at the right and let r_2 represent the radius of the crankshaft passing through it. If the formula for the area of a circle is $A = \pi r^2$, write a simplified, factored expression for the area of the cross section of the flywheel outside the crankshaft.

5-5 Practice

Roots of Real Numbers

Use a calculator to approximate each value to three decimal places.

1. $\sqrt{7.8}$

2. $-\sqrt{89}$

3. $\sqrt[3]{25}$

4. $\sqrt[3]{-4}$

5. $\sqrt[4]{1.1}$

6. $\sqrt[5]{-0.1}$

7. $\sqrt[6]{5555}$

8. $\sqrt[4]{(0.94)^2}$

Simplify.

9. $\sqrt{0.81}$

10. $-\sqrt{324}$

11. $-\sqrt[4]{256}$

12. $\sqrt[6]{64}$

13. $\sqrt[3]{-64}$

14. $\sqrt[3]{0.512}$

15. $\sqrt[5]{-243}$

16. $-\sqrt[4]{1296}$

17. $\sqrt[5]{\dfrac{-1024}{243}}$

18. $\sqrt[5]{243x^{10}}$

19. $\sqrt{(14a)^2}$

20. $\sqrt{-(14a)^2}$

21. $\sqrt{49m^2t^8}$

22. $\sqrt{\dfrac{16m^2}{25}}$

23. $\sqrt[3]{-64r^6w^{15}}$

24. $\sqrt{(2x)^8}$

25. $-\sqrt[4]{625s^8}$

26. $\sqrt[3]{216p^3q^9}$

27. $\sqrt{676x^4y^6}$

28. $\sqrt[3]{-27x^9y^{12}}$

29. $-\sqrt{144m^8n^6}$

30. $\sqrt[5]{-32x^5y^{10}}$

31. $\sqrt[6]{(m+4)^6}$

32. $\sqrt[3]{(2x+1)^3}$

33. $-\sqrt{49a^{10}b^{16}}$

34. $\sqrt[4]{(x-5)^8}$

35. $\sqrt[3]{343d^6}$

36. $\sqrt{x^2+10x+25}$

37. RADIANT TEMPERATURE Thermal sensors measure an object's *radiant* temperature, which is the amount of energy radiated by the object. The *internal* temperature of an object is called its *kinetic* temperature. The formula $T_r = T_k\sqrt[4]{e}$ relates an object's radiant temperature T_r to its kinetic temperature T_k. The variable e in the formula is a measure of how well the object radiates energy. If an object's kinetic temperature is 30°C and $e = 0.94$, what is the object's radiant temperature to the nearest tenth of a degree?

38. HERO'S FORMULA Salvatore is buying fertilizer for his triangular garden. He knows the lengths of all three sides, so he is using Hero's formula to find the area. Hero's formula states that the area of a triangle is $\sqrt{s(s-a)(s-b)(s-c)}$, where a, b, and c are the lengths of the sides of the triangle and s is half the perimeter of the triangle. If the lengths of the sides of Salvatore's garden are 15 feet, 17 feet, and 20 feet, what is the area of the garden? Round your answer to the nearest whole number.

5-6 Practice

Radical Expressions

Simplify.

1. $\sqrt{540}$

2. $\sqrt[3]{-432}$

3. $\sqrt[3]{128}$

4. $-\sqrt[4]{405}$

5. $\sqrt[3]{-5000}$

6. $\sqrt[5]{-1215}$

7. $\sqrt[3]{125t^6w^2}$

8. $\sqrt[4]{48v^8z^{13}}$

9. $\sqrt[3]{8g^3k^8}$

10. $\sqrt{45x^3y^8}$

11. $\sqrt{\dfrac{11}{9}}$

12. $\sqrt[3]{\dfrac{216}{24}}$

13. $\sqrt{\dfrac{1}{128}c^4d^7}$

14. $\sqrt{\dfrac{9a^5}{64b^4}}$

15. $\sqrt[4]{\dfrac{8}{9a^3}}$

16. $(3\sqrt{15})(-4\sqrt{45})$

17. $(2\sqrt{24})(7\sqrt{18})$

18. $\sqrt{810} + \sqrt{240} - \sqrt{250}$

19. $6\sqrt{20} + 8\sqrt{5} - 5\sqrt{45}$

20. $8\sqrt{48} - 6\sqrt{75} + 7\sqrt{80}$

21. $(3\sqrt{2} + 2\sqrt{3})^2$

22. $(3 - \sqrt{7})^2$

23. $(\sqrt{5} - \sqrt{6})(\sqrt{5} + \sqrt{2})$

24. $(\sqrt{2} + \sqrt{10})(\sqrt{2} - \sqrt{10})$

25. $(1 + \sqrt{6})(5 - \sqrt{7})$

26. $(\sqrt{3} + 4\sqrt{7})^2$

27. $(\sqrt{108} - 6\sqrt{3})^2$

28. $\dfrac{\sqrt{3}}{\sqrt{5} - 2}$

29. $\dfrac{6}{\sqrt{2} - 1}$

30. $\dfrac{5 + \sqrt{3}}{4 + \sqrt{3}}$

31. $\dfrac{3 + \sqrt{2}}{2 - \sqrt{2}}$

32. $\dfrac{3 + \sqrt{6}}{5 - \sqrt{24}}$

33. $\dfrac{3 + \sqrt{x}}{2 - \sqrt{x}}$

34. **BRAKING** The formula $s = 2\sqrt{5\ell}$ estimates the speed s in miles per hour of a car when it leaves skid marks ℓ feet long. Use the formula to write a simplified expression for s if $\ell = 85$. Then evaluate s to the nearest mile per hour.

35. **PYTHAGOREAN THEOREM** The measures of the legs of a right triangle can be represented by the expressions $6x^2y$ and $9x^2y$. Use the Pythagorean Theorem to find a simplified expression for the measure of the hypotenuse.

Glencoe Algebra 2

5-7 Practice

Rational Exponents

Write each expression in radical form.

1. $5^{\frac{1}{3}}$ **2.** $6^{\frac{2}{5}}$ **3.** $m^{\frac{4}{7}}$ **4.** $(n^3)^{\frac{2}{5}}$

Write each radical using rational exponents.

5. $\sqrt{79}$ **6.** $\sqrt[4]{153}$ **7.** $\sqrt[3]{27m^6 n^4}$ **8.** $5\sqrt{2a^{10}b}$

Evaluate each expression.

9. $81^{\frac{1}{4}}$ **10.** $1024^{-\frac{1}{5}}$ **11.** $8^{-\frac{5}{3}}$

12. $-256^{-\frac{3}{4}}$ **13.** $(-64)^{-\frac{2}{3}}$ **14.** $27^{\frac{1}{3}} \cdot 27^{\frac{4}{3}}$

15. $\left(\dfrac{125}{216}\right)^{\frac{2}{3}}$ **16.** $\dfrac{64^{\frac{2}{3}}}{343^{\frac{2}{3}}}$ **17.** $\left(25^{\frac{1}{2}}\right)\left(-64^{-\frac{1}{3}}\right)$

Simplify each expression.

18. $g^{\frac{4}{7}} \cdot g^{\frac{3}{7}}$ **19.** $s^{\frac{3}{4}} \cdot s^{\frac{13}{4}}$ **20.** $\left(u^{-\frac{1}{3}}\right)^{-\frac{4}{5}}$ **21.** $y^{-\frac{1}{2}}$

22. $b^{-\frac{3}{5}}$ **23.** $\dfrac{q^{\frac{3}{5}}}{q^{\frac{2}{5}}}$ **24.** $\dfrac{t^{\frac{2}{3}}}{5t^{\frac{1}{2}} \cdot t^{-\frac{3}{4}}}$ **25.** $\dfrac{2z^{\frac{1}{2}}}{z^{\frac{1}{2}} - 1}$

26. $\sqrt[10]{8^5}$ **27.** $\sqrt{12} \cdot \sqrt[5]{12^3}$ **28.** $\sqrt[4]{6} \cdot 3\sqrt[4]{6}$ **29.** $\dfrac{a}{\sqrt{3b}}$

30. ELECTRICITY The amount of current in amperes I that an appliance uses can be calculated using the formula $I = \left(\dfrac{P}{R}\right)^{\frac{1}{2}}$, where P is the power in watts and R is the resistance in ohms. How much current does an appliance use if $P = 500$ watts and $R = 10$ ohms? Round your answer to the nearest tenth.

31. BUSINESS A company that produces DVDs uses the formula $C = 88n^{\frac{1}{3}} + 330$ to calculate the cost C in dollars of producing n DVDs per day. What is the company's cost to produce 150 DVDs per day? Round your answer to the nearest dollar.

5-8 Practice

Radical Equations and Inequalities

Solve each equation or inequality.

1. $\sqrt{x} = 8$

2. $4 - \sqrt{x} = 3$

3. $\sqrt{2p} + 3 = 10$

4. $4\sqrt{3h} - 2 = 0$

5. $c^{\frac{1}{2}} + 6 = 9$

6. $18 + 7h^{\frac{1}{2}} = 12$

7. $\sqrt[3]{d} + 2 = 7$

8. $\sqrt[5]{w} - 7 = 1$

9. $6 + \sqrt[3]{q - 4} = 9$

10. $\sqrt[4]{y - 9} + 4 = 0$

11. $\sqrt{2m - 6} - 16 = 0$

12. $\sqrt[3]{4m + 1} - 2 = 2$

13. $\sqrt{8n - 5} - 1 = 2$

14. $\sqrt{1 - 4t} - 8 = -6$

15. $\sqrt{2t - 5} - 3 = 3$

16. $(7v - 2)^{\frac{1}{4}} + 12 = 7$

17. $(3g + 1)^{\frac{1}{2}} - 6 = 4$

18. $(6u - 5)^{\frac{1}{3}} + 2 = -3$

19. $\sqrt{2d - 5} = \sqrt{d - 1}$

20. $\sqrt{4r - 6} = \sqrt{r}$

21. $\sqrt{6x - 4} = \sqrt{2x + 10}$

22. $\sqrt{2x + 5} = \sqrt{2x + 1}$

23. $3\sqrt{a} \geq 12$

24. $\sqrt{z + 5} + 4 \leq 13$

25. $8 + \sqrt{2q} \leq 5$

26. $\sqrt{2a - 3} < 5$

27. $9 - \sqrt{c + 4} \leq 6$

28. $\sqrt[3]{x - 1} < -2$

29. **STATISTICS** Statisticians use the formula $\sigma = \sqrt{v}$ to calculate a standard deviation σ, where v is the variance of a data set. Find the variance when the standard deviation is 15.

30. **GRAVITATION** Helena drops a ball from 25 feet above a lake. The formula $t = \frac{1}{4}\sqrt{25 - h}$ describes the time t in seconds that the ball is h feet above the water. How many feet above the water will the ball be after 1 second?

5-9 Practice

Complex Numbers

Simplify.

1. $\sqrt{-49}$

2. $6\sqrt{-12}$

3. $\sqrt{-121s^8}$

4. $\sqrt{-36a^3b^4}$

5. $\sqrt{-8} \cdot \sqrt{-32}$

6. $\sqrt{-15} \cdot \sqrt{-25}$

7. $(-3i)(4i)(-5i)$

8. $(7i)^2(6i)$

9. i^{42}

10. i^{55}

11. i^{89}

12. $(5 - 2i) + (-13 - 8i)$

13. $(7 - 6i) + (9 + 11i)$

14. $(-12 + 48i) + (15 + 21i)$

15. $(10 + 15i) - (48 - 30i)$

16. $(28 - 4i) - (10 - 30i)$

17. $(6 - 4i)(6 + 4i)$

18. $(8 - 11i)(8 - 11i)$

19. $(4 + 3i)(2 - 5i)$

20. $(7 + 2i)(9 - 6i)$

21. $\dfrac{6 + 5i}{-2i}$

22. $\dfrac{2}{7 - 8i}$

23. $\dfrac{3 - i}{2 - i}$

24. $\dfrac{2 - 4i}{1 + 3i}$

Solve each equation.

25. $5n^2 + 35 = 0$

26. $2m^2 + 10 = 0$

27. $4m^2 + 76 = 0$

28. $-2m^2 - 6 = 0$

29. $-5m^2 - 65 = 0$

30. $\dfrac{3}{4}x^2 + 12 = 0$

Find the values of m and n that make each equation true.

31. $15 - 28i = 3m + 4ni$

32. $(6 - m) + 3ni = -12 + 27i$

33. $(3m + 4) + (3 - n)i = 16 - 3i$

34. $(7 + n) + (4m - 10)i = 3 - 6i$

35. **ELECTRICITY** The impedance in one part of a series circuit is $1 + 3j$ ohms and the impedance in another part of the circuit is $7 - 5j$ ohms. Add these complex numbers to find the total impedance in the circuit.

36. **ELECTRICITY** Using the formula $E = IZ$, find the voltage E in a circuit when the current I is $3 - j$ amps and the impedance Z is $3 + 2j$ ohms.

6-1 Practice

Graphing Quadratic Functions

Complete parts a–c for each quadratic function.

a. Find the y-intercept, the equation of the axis of symmetry, and the x-coordinate of the vertex.

b. Make a table of values that includes the vertex.

c. Use this information to graph the function.

1. $f(x) = x^2 - 8x + 15$ 2. $f(x) = -x^2 - 4x + 12$ 3. $f(x) = 2x^2 - 2x + 1$

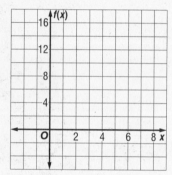   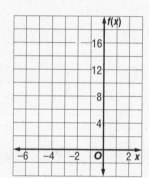   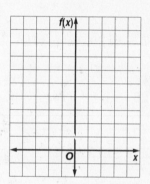

Determine whether each function has a maximum or a minimum value. Then find the maximum or minimum value of each function.

4. $f(x) = x^2 + 2x - 8$ 5. $f(x) = x^2 - 6x + 14$ 6. $v(x) = -x^2 + 14x - 57$

7. $f(x) = 2x^2 + 4x - 6$ 8. $f(x) = -x^2 + 4x - 1$ 9. $f(x) = -\frac{2}{3}x^2 + 8x - 24$

10. **GRAVITATION** From 4 feet above a swimming pool, Susan throws a ball upward with a velocity of 32 feet per second. The height $h(t)$ of the ball t seconds after Susan throws it is given by $h(t) = -16t^2 + 32t + 4$. Find the maximum height reached by the ball and the time that this height is reached.

11. **HEALTH CLUBS** Last year, the SportsTime Athletic Club charged $20 to participate in an aerobics class. Seventy people attended the classes. The club wants to increase the class price this year. They expect to lose one customer for each $1 increase in the price.

a. What price should the club charge to maximize the income from the aerobics classes?

b. What is the maximum income the SportsTime Athletic Club can expect to make?

6-2 Practice

Solving Quadratic Equations By Graphing

Use the related graph of each equation to determine its solutions.

1. $-3x^2 + 3 = 0$

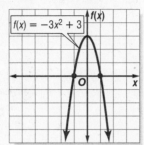

$f(x) = -3x^2 + 3$

2. $3x^2 + x + 3 = 0$

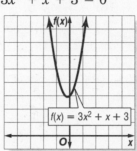

$f(x) = 3x^2 + x + 3$

3. $x^2 - 3x + 2 = 0$

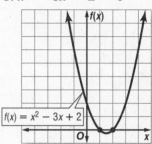

$f(x) = x^2 - 3x + 2$

Solve each equation by graphing. If exact roots cannot be found, state the consecutive integers between which the roots are located.

4. $-2x^2 - 6x + 5 = 0$

5. $x^2 + 10x + 24 = 0$

6. $2x^2 - x - 6 = 0$

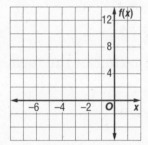

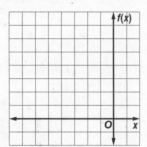

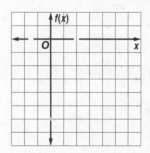

Use a quadratic equation to find two real numbers that satisfy each situation, or show that no such numbers exist.

7. Their sum is 1, and their product is -6.

8. Their sum is 5, and their product is 8.

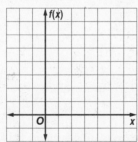

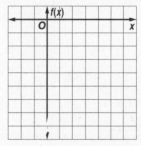

For Exercises 9 and 10, use the formula $h(t) = v_0 t - 16t^2$, where $h(t)$ is the height of an object in feet, v_0 is the object's initial velocity in feet per second, and t is the time in seconds.

9. BASEBALL Marta throws a baseball with an initial upward velocity of 60 feet per second. Ignoring Marta's height, how long after she releases the ball will it hit the ground?

10. VOLCANOES A volcanic eruption blasts a boulder upward with an initial velocity of 240 feet per second. How long will it take the boulder to hit the ground if it lands at the same elevation from which it was ejected?

6-3 Practice

Solving Quadratic Equations by Factoring

Solve each equation by factoring.

1. $x^2 - 4x - 12 = 0$ **2.** $x^2 - 16x + 64 = 0$ **3.** $x^2 - 20x + 100 = 0$

4. $x^2 - 6x + 8 = 0$ **5.** $x^2 + 3x + 2 = 0$ **6.** $x^2 - 9x + 14 = 0$

7. $x^2 - 4x = 0$ **8.** $7x^2 = 4x$ **9.** $x^2 + 25 = 10x$

10. $10x^2 = 9x$ **11.** $x^2 = 2x + 99$

12. $x^2 + 12x = -36$ **13.** $5x^2 - 35x + 60 = 0$

14. $36x^2 = 25$ **15.** $2x^2 - 8x - 90 = 0$

16. $3x^2 + 2x - 1 = 0$ **17.** $6x^2 = 9x$

18. $3x^2 + 24x + 45 = 0$ **19.** $15x^2 + 19x + 6 = 0$

20. $3x^2 - 8x = -4$ **21.** $6x^2 = 5x + 6$

Write a quadratic equation with the given roots. Write the equation in the form $ax^2 + bx + c = 0$, where a, b, and c are integers.

22. $7, 2$ **23.** $0, 3$ **24.** $-5, 8$

25. $-7, -8$ **26.** $-6, -3$ **27.** $3, -4$

28. $1, \dfrac{1}{2}$ **29.** $\dfrac{1}{3}, 2$ **30.** $0, -\dfrac{7}{2}$

31. $\dfrac{1}{3}, -3$ **32.** $4, \dfrac{1}{3}$ **33.** $-\dfrac{2}{3}, -\dfrac{4}{5}$

34. NUMBER THEORY Find two consecutive even positive integers whose product is 624.

35. NUMBER THEORY Find two consecutive odd positive integers whose product is 323.

36. GEOMETRY The length of a rectangle is 2 feet more than its width. Find the dimensions of the rectangle if its area is 63 square feet.

37. PHOTOGRAPHY The length and width of a 6-inch by 8-inch photograph are reduced by the same amount to make a new photograph whose area is half that of the original. By how many inches will the dimensions of the photograph have to be reduced?

6-4 Practice

Completing the Square

Solve each equation by using the Square Root Property.

1. $x^2 + 8x + 16 = 1$

2. $x^2 + 6x + 9 = 1$

3. $x^2 + 10x + 25 = 16$

4. $x^2 - 14x + 49 = 9$

5. $4x^2 + 12x + 9 = 4$

6. $x^2 - 8x + 16 = 8$

7. $x^2 - 6x + 9 = 5$

8. $x^2 - 2x + 1 = 2$

9. $9x^2 - 6x + 1 = 2$

Find the value of c that makes each trinomial a perfect square. Then write the trinomial as a perfect square.

10. $x^2 + 12x + c$

11. $x^2 - 20x + c$

12. $x^2 + 11x + c$

13. $x^2 + 0.8x + c$

14. $x^2 - 2.2x + c$

15. $x^2 - 0.36x + c$

16. $x^2 + \frac{5}{6}x + c$

17. $x^2 - \frac{1}{4}x + c$

18. $x^2 - \frac{5}{3}x + c$

Solve each equation by completing the square.

19. $x^2 + 6x + 8 = 0$

20. $3x^2 + x - 2 = 0$

21. $3x^2 - 5x + 2 = 0$

22. $x^2 + 18 = 9x$

23. $x^2 - 14x + 19 = 0$

24. $x^2 + 16x - 7 = 0$

25. $2x^2 + 8x - 3 = 0$

26. $x^2 + x - 5 = 0$

27. $2x^2 - 10x + 5 = 0$

28. $x^2 + 3x + 6 = 0$

29. $2x^2 + 5x + 6 = 0$

30. $7x^2 + 6x + 2 = 0$

31. GEOMETRY When the dimensions of a cube are reduced by 4 inches on each side, the surface area of the new cube is 864 square inches. What were the dimensions of the original cube?

32. INVESTMENTS The amount of money A in an account in which P dollars is invested for 2 years is given by the formula $A = P(1 + r)^2$, where r is the interest rate compounded annually. If an investment of $800 in the account grows to $882 in two years, at what interest rate was it invested?

6-5 Practice

The Quadratic Formula and the Discriminant

Complete parts a–c for each quadratic equation.

a. Find the value of the discriminant.

b. Describe the number and type of roots.

c. Find the exact solutions by using the Quadratic Formula.

1. $x^2 - 16x + 64 = 0$ **2.** $x^2 = 3x$ **3.** $9x^2 - 24x + 16 = 0$

4. $x^2 - 3x = 40$ **5.** $3x^2 + 9x - 2 = 0$ **6.** $2x^2 + 7x = 0$

7. $5x^2 - 2x + 4 = 0$ **8.** $12x^2 - x - 6 = 0$ **9.** $7x^2 + 6x + 2 = 0$

10. $12x^2 + 2x - 4 = 0$ **11.** $6x^2 - 2x - 1 = 0$ **12.** $x^2 + 3x + 6 = 0$

13. $4x^2 - 3x - 6 = 0$ **14.** $16x^2 - 8x + 1 = 0$ **15.** $2x^2 - 5x - 6 = 0$

Solve each equation by using the method of your choice. Find exact solutions.

16. $7x^2 - 5x = 0$ **17.** $4x^2 - 9 = 0$

18. $3x^2 + 8x = 3$ **19.** $x^2 - 21 = 4x$

20. $3x^2 - 13x + 4 = 0$ **21.** $15x^2 + 22x = -8$

22. $x^2 - 6x + 3 = 0$ **23.** $x^2 - 14x + 53 = 0$

24. $3x^2 = -54$ **25.** $25x^2 - 20x - 6 = 0$

26. $4x^2 - 4x + 17 = 0$ **27.** $8x - 1 = 4x^2$

28. $x^2 = 4x - 15$ **29.** $4x^2 - 12x + 7 = 0$

30. GRAVITATION The height $h(t)$ in feet of an object t seconds after it is propelled straight up from the ground with an initial velocity of 60 feet per second is modeled by the equation $h(t) = -16t^2 + 60t$. At what times will the object be at a height of 56 feet?

31. STOPPING DISTANCE The formula $d = 0.05s^2 + 1.1s$ estimates the minimum stopping distance d in feet for a car traveling s miles per hour. If a car stops in 200 feet, what is the fastest it could have been traveling when the driver applied the brakes?

6-6 Practice

Analyzing Graphs of Quadratic Functions

Write each quadratic function in vertex form, if not already in that form. Then identify the vertex, axis of symmetry, and direction of opening.

1. $y = -6(x + 2)^2 - 1$

2. $y = 2x^2 + 2$

3. $y = -4x^2 + 8x$

4. $y = x^2 + 10x + 20$

5. $y = 2x^2 + 12x + 18$

6. $y = 3x^2 - 6x + 5$

7. $y = -2x^2 - 16x - 32$

8. $y = -3x^2 + 18x - 21$

9. $y = 2x^2 + 16x + 29$

Graph each function.

10. $y = (x + 3)^2 - 1$

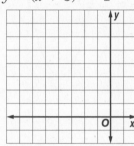

11. $y = -x^2 + 6x - 5$

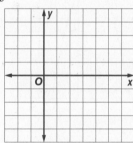

12. $y = 2x^2 - 2x + 1$

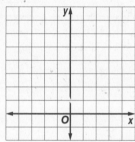

Write an equation for the parabola with the given vertex that passes through the given point.

13. vertex: $(1, 3)$
point: $(-2, -15)$

14. vertex: $(-3, 0)$
point: $(3, 18)$

15. vertex: $(10, -4)$
point: $(5, 6)$

16. Write an equation for a parabola with vertex at $(4, 4)$ and x-intercept 6.

17. Write an equation for a parabola with vertex at $(-3, -1)$ and y-intercept 2.

18. BASEBALL The height h of a baseball t seconds after being hit is given by $h(t) = -16t^2 + 80t + 3$. What is the maximum height that the baseball reaches, and when does this occur?

19. SCULPTURE A modern sculpture in a park contains a parabolic arc that starts at the ground and reaches a maximum height of 10 feet after a horizontal distance of 4 feet. Write a quadratic function in vertex form that describes the shape of the outside of the arc, where y is the height of a point on the arc and x is its horizontal distance from the left-hand starting point of the arc.

10 ft

4 ft

41

6-7 Practice

Graphing and Solving Quadratic Inequalities

Graph each inequality.

1. $y \leq x^2 + 4$

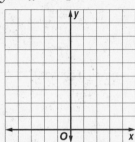

2. $y > x^2 + 6x + 6$

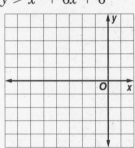

3. $y < 2x^2 - 4x - 2$

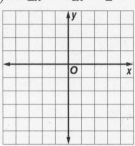

Use the graph of its related function to write the solutions of each inequality.

4. $x^2 - 8x > 0$

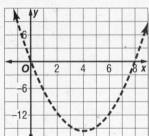

5. $-x^2 - 2x + 3 \geq 0$

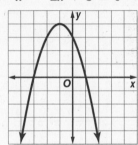

6. $x^2 - 9x + 14 \leq 0$

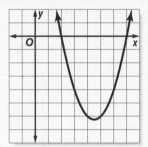

Solve each inequality algebraically.

7. $x^2 - x - 20 > 0$

8. $x^2 - 10x + 16 < 0$

9. $x^2 + 4x + 5 \leq 0$

10. $x^2 + 14x + 49 \geq 0$

11. $x^2 - 5x > 14$

12. $-x^2 - 15 \geq 8x$

13. $-x^2 + 5x - 7 \leq 0$

14. $9x^2 + 36x + 36 \leq 0$

15. $9x \leq 12x^2$

16. $4x^2 + 4x + 1 > 0$

17. $5x^2 + 10 \geq 27x$

18. $9x^2 + 31x + 12 \leq 0$

19. FENCING Vanessa has 180 feet of fencing that she intends to use to build a rectangular play area for her dog. She wants the play area to enclose at least 1800 square feet. What are the possible widths of the play area?

20. BUSINESS A bicycle maker sold 300 bicycles last year at a profit of $300 each. The maker wants to increase the profit margin this year, but predicts that each $20 increase in profit will reduce the number of bicycles sold by 10. How many $20 increases in profit can the maker add in and expect to make a total profit of at least $100,000?

7-1 Practice

Polynomial Functions

State the degree and leading coefficient of each polynomial in one variable. If it is not a polynomial in one variable, explain why.

1. $(3x^2 + 1)(2x^2 - 9)$

2. $\frac{1}{5}a^3 - \frac{3}{5}a^2 + \frac{4}{5}a$

3. $\frac{2}{m^2} + 3m - 12$

4. $27 + 3xy^3 - 12x^2y^2 - 10y$

Find $p(-2)$ and $p(3)$ for each function.

5. $p(x) = x^3 - x^5$

6. $p(x) = -7x^2 + 5x + 9$

7. $p(x) = -x^5 + 4x^3$

8. $p(x) = 3x^3 - x^2 + 2x - 5$

9. $p(x) = x^4 + \frac{1}{2}x^3 - \frac{1}{2}x$

10. $p(x) = \frac{1}{3}x^3 + \frac{2}{3}x^2 + 3x$

If $p(x) = 3x^2 - 4$ and $r(x) = 2x^2 - 5x + 1$, find each value.

11. $p(8a)$

12. $r(a^2)$

13. $-5r(2a)$

14. $r(x + 2)$

15. $p(x^2 - 1)$

16. $5[p(x + 2)]$

For each graph,
a. describe the end behavior,
b. determine whether it represents an odd-degree or an even-degree polynomial function, and
c. state the number of real zeroes.

17.
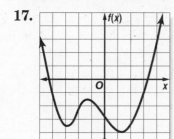

18.
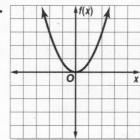

19.
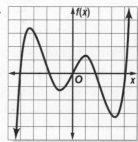

20. WIND CHILL The function $C(s) = 0.013s^2 - s - 7$ estimates the wind chill temperature $C(s)$ at 0°F for wind speeds s from 5 to 30 miles per hour. Estimate the wind chill temperature at 0°F if the wind speed is 20 miles per hour.

7-2 Practice

Graphing Polynomial Functions

Complete each of the following.
a. Graph each function by making a table of values.
b. Determine consecutive values of x between which each real zero is located.
c. Estimate the x-coordinates at which the relative and relative minima occur.

1. $f(x) = -x^3 + 3x^2 - 3$

x	f(x)
-2	
-1	
0	
1	
2	
3	
4	

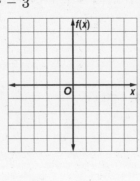

2. $f(x) = x^3 - 1.5x^2 - 6x + 1$

x	f(x)
-2	
-1	
0	
1	
2	
3	
4	

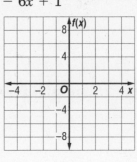

3. $f(x) = 0.75x^4 + x^3 - 3x^2 + 4$

x	f(x)

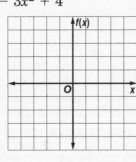

4. $f(x) = x^4 + 4x^3 + 6x^2 + 4x - 3$

x	f(x)

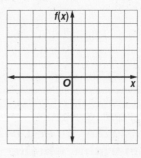

PRICES For Exercises 5 and 6, use the following information.

The Consumer Price Index (CPI) gives the relative price
for a fixed set of goods and services. The CPI from
September, 2000 to July, 2001 is shown in the graph.

Source: U. S. Bureau of Labor Statistics

5. Describe the turning points of the graph.

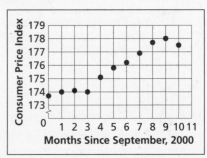

6. If the graph were modeled by a polynomial equation,
what is the least degree the equation could have?

7. LABOR A town's jobless rate can be modeled by (1, 3.3), (2, 4.9), (3, 5.3), (4, 6.4), (5, 4.5),
(6, 5.6), (7, 2.5), (8, 2.7). How many turning points would the graph of a polynomial
function through these points have? Describe them.

7-3 Practice

Solving Equations Using Quadratic Techniques

Write each expression in quadratic form, if possible.

1. $10b^4 + 3b^2 - 11$

2. $-5x^8 + x^2 + 6$

3. $28d^6 + 25d^3$

4. $4s^8 + 4s^4 + 7$

5. $500x^4 - x^2$

6. $8b^5 - 8b^3 - 1$

7. $32w^5 - 56w^3 + 8w$

8. $e^{\frac{2}{3}} + 7e^{\frac{1}{3}} - 10$

9. $x^{\frac{1}{5}} + 29x^{\frac{1}{10}} + 2$

Solve each equation.

10. $y^4 - 7y^3 - 18y^2 = 0$

11. $s^5 + 4s^4 - 32s^3 = 0$

12. $m^4 - 625 = 0$

13. $n^4 - 49n^2 = 0$

14. $x^4 - 50x^2 + 49 = 0$

15. $t^4 - 21t^2 + 80 = 0$

16. $4r^6 - 9r^4 = 0$

17. $x^4 - 24 = -2x^2$

18. $d^4 = 16d^2 - 48$

19. $t^3 - 343 = 0$

20. $x^{\frac{1}{2}} - 5x^{\frac{1}{4}} + 6 = 0$

21. $x^{\frac{4}{3}} - 29x^{\frac{2}{3}} + 100 = 0$

22. $y^3 - 28y^{\frac{3}{2}} + 27 = 0$

23. $n - 10\sqrt{n} + 25 = 0$

24. $w - 12\sqrt{w} + 27 = 0$

25. $x - 2\sqrt{x} - 80 = 0$

26. **PHYSICS** A proton in a magnetic field follows a path on a coordinate grid modeled by the function $f(x) = x^4 - 2x^2 - 15$. What are the x-coordinates of the points on the grid where the proton crosses the x-axis?

27. **SURVEYING** Vista county is setting aside a large parcel of land to preserve it as open space. The county has hired Meghan's surveying firm to survey the parcel, which is in the shape of a right triangle. The longer leg of the triangle measures 5 miles less than the square of the shorter leg, and the hypotenuse of the triangle measures 13 miles less than twice the square of the shorter leg. The length of each boundary is a whole number. Find the length of each boundary.

7-4 Practice

The Remainder and Factor Theorems

Use synthetic substitution to find $f(-3)$ and $f(4)$ for each function.

1. $f(x) = x^2 + 2x + 3$

2. $f(x) = x^2 - 5x + 10$

3. $f(x) = x^2 - 5x - 4$

4. $f(x) = x^3 - x^2 - 2x + 3$

5. $f(x) = x^3 + 2x^2 + 5$

6. $f(x) = x^3 - 6x^2 + 2x$

7. $f(x) = x^3 - 2x^2 - 2x + 8$

8. $f(x) = x^3 - x^2 + 4x - 4$

9. $f(x) = x^3 + 3x^2 + 2x - 50$

10. $f(x) = x^4 + x^3 - 3x^2 - x + 12$

11. $f(x) = x^4 - 2x^2 - x + 7$

12. $f(x) = 2x^4 - 3x^3 + 4x^2 - 2x + 1$

13. $f(x) = 2x^4 - x^3 + 2x^2 - 26$

14. $f(x) = 3x^4 - 4x^3 + 3x^2 - 5x - 3$

15. $f(x) = x^5 + 7x^3 - 4x - 10$

16. $f(x) = x^6 + 2x^5 - x^4 + x^3 - 9x^2 + 20$

Given a polynomial and one of its factors, find the remaining factors of the polynomial. Some factors may not be binomials.

17. $x^3 + 3x^2 - 6x - 8; x - 2$

18. $x^3 + 7x^2 + 7x - 15; x - 1$

19. $x^3 - 9x^2 + 27x - 27; x - 3$

20. $x^3 - x^2 - 8x + 12; x + 3$

21. $x^3 + 5x^2 - 2x - 24; x - 2$

22. $x^3 - x^2 - 14x + 24; x + 4$

23. $3x^3 - 4x^2 - 17x + 6; x + 2$

24. $4x^3 - 12x^2 - x + 3; x - 3$

25. $18x^3 + 9x^2 - 2x - 1; 2x + 1$

26. $6x^3 + 5x^2 - 3x - 2; 3x - 2$

27. $x^5 + x^4 - 5x^3 - 5x^2 + 4x + 4; x + 1$

28. $x^5 - 2x^4 + 4x^3 - 8x^2 - 5x + 10; x - 2$

29. POPULATION The projected population in thousands for a city over the next several years can be estimated by the function $P(x) = x^3 + 2x^2 - 8x + 520$, where x is the number of years since 2000. Use synthetic substitution to estimate the population for 2005.

30. VOLUME The volume of water in a rectangular swimming pool can be modeled by the polynomial $2x^3 - 9x^2 + 7x + 6$. If the depth of the pool is given by the polynomial $2x + 1$, what polynomials express the length and width of the pool?

7-5 Practice

Roots and Zeros

Solve each equation. State the number and type of roots.

1. $-9x - 15 = 0$

2. $x^4 - 5x^2 + 4 = 0$

3. $x^5 = 81x$

4. $x^3 + x^2 - 3x - 3 = 0$

5. $x^3 + 6x + 20 = 0$

6. $x^4 - x^3 - x^2 - x - 2 = 0$

State the possible number of positive real zeros, negative real zeros, and imaginary zeros of each function.

7. $f(x) = 4x^3 - 2x^2 + x + 3$

8. $p(x) = 2x^4 - 2x^3 + 2x^2 - x - 1$

9. $q(x) = 3x^4 + x^3 - 3x^2 + 7x + 5$

10. $h(x) = 7x^4 + 3x^3 - 2x^2 - x + 1$

Find all the zeros of each function.

11. $h(x) = 2x^3 + 3x^2 - 65x + 84$

12. $p(x) = x^3 - 3x^2 + 9x - 7$

13. $h(x) = x^3 - 7x^2 + 17x - 15$

14. $q(x) = x^4 + 50x^2 + 49$

15. $g(x) = x^4 + 4x^3 - 3x^2 - 14x - 8$

16. $f(x) = x^4 - 6x^3 + 6x^2 + 24x - 40$

Write a polynomial function of least degree with integral coefficients that has the given zeros.

17. $-5, 3i$

18. $-2, 3 + i$

19. $-1, 4, 3i$

20. $2, 5, 1 + i$

21. **CRAFTS** Stephan has a set of plans to build a wooden box. He wants to reduce the volume of the box to 105 cubic inches. He would like to reduce the length of each dimension in the plan by the same amount. The plans call for the box to be 10 inches by 8 inches by 6 inches. Write and solve a polynomial equation to find out how much Stephen should take from each dimension.

7-6 Practice

Rational Zero Theorem

List all of the possible rational zeros of each function.

1. $h(x) = x^3 - 5x^2 + 2x + 12$

2. $s(x) = x^4 - 8x^3 + 7x - 14$

3. $f(x) = 3x^5 - 5x^2 + x + 6$

4. $p(x) = 3x^2 + x + 7$

5. $g(x) = 5x^3 + x^2 - x + 8$

6. $q(x) = 6x^5 + x^3 - 3$

Find all of the rational zeros of each function.

7. $q(x) = x^3 + 3x^2 - 6x - 8 = 0$

8. $v(x) = x^3 - 9x^2 + 27x - 27$

9. $c(x) = x^3 - x^2 - 8x + 12$

10. $f(x) = x^4 - 49x^2$

11. $h(x) = x^3 - 7x^2 + 17x - 15$

12. $b(x) = x^3 + 6x + 20$

13. $f(x) = x^3 - 6x^2 + 4x - 24$

14. $g(x) = 2x^3 + 3x^2 - 4x - 4$

15. $h(x) = 2x^3 - 7x^2 - 21x + 54 = 0$

16. $z(x) = x^4 - 3x^3 + 5x^2 - 27x - 36$

17. $d(x) = x^4 + x^3 + 16$

18. $n(x) = x^4 - 2x^3 - 3$

19. $p(x) = 2x^4 - 7x^3 + 4x^2 + 7x - 6$

20. $q(x) = 6x^4 + 29x^3 + 40x^2 + 7x - 12$

Find all of the zeros of each function.

21. $f(x) = 2x^4 + 7x^3 - 2x^2 - 19x - 12$

22. $q(x) = x^4 - 4x^3 + x^2 + 16x - 20$

23. $h(x) = x^6 - 8x^3$

24. $g(x) = x^6 - 1$

25. TRAVEL The height of a box that Joan is shipping is 3 inches less than the width of the box. The length is 2 inches more than twice the width. The volume of the box is 1540 in³. What are the dimensions of the box?

26. GEOMETRY The height of a square pyramid is 3 meters shorter than the side of its base. If the volume of the pyramid is 432 m³, how tall is it? Use the formula $V = \frac{1}{3}Bh$.

7-7 Practice

Operations on Functions

Find $(f + g)(x)$, $(f - g)(x)$, $(f \cdot g)(x)$, and $\left(\dfrac{f}{g}\right)(x)$ for each $f(x)$ and $g(x)$.

1. $f(x) = 2x + 1$
$g(x) = x - 3$

2. $f(x) = 8x^2$
$g(x) = \dfrac{1}{x^2}$

3. $f(x) = x^2 + 7x + 12$
$g(x) = x^2 - 9$

For each set of ordered pairs, find $f \circ g$ and $g \circ f$ if they exist.

4. $f = \{(-9, -1), (-1, 0), (3, 4)\}$
$g = \{(0, -9), (-1, 3), (4, -1)\}$

5. $f = \{(-4, 3), (0, -2), (1, -2)\}$
$g = \{(-2, 0), (3, 1)\}$

6. $f = \{(-4, -5), (0, 3), (1, 6)\}$
$g = \{(6, 1), (-5, 0), (3, -4)\}$

7. $f = \{(0, -3), (1, -3), (6, 8)\}$
$g = \{(8, 2), (-3, 0), (-3, 1)\}$

Find $[g \circ h](x)$ and $[h \circ g](x)$.

8. $g(x) = 3x$
$h(x) = x - 4$

9. $g(x) = -8x$
$h(x) = 2x + 3$

10. $g(x) = x + 6$
$h(x) = 3x^2$

11. $g(x) = x + 3$
$h(x) = 2x^2$

12. $g(x) = -2x$
$h(x) = x^2 + 3x + 2$

13. $g(x) = x - 2$
$h(x) = 3x^2 + 1$

If $f(x) = x^2$, $g(x) = 5x$, and $h(x) = x + 4$, find each value.

14. $f[g(1)]$

15. $g[h(-2)]$

16. $h[f(4)]$

17. $f[h(-9)]$

18. $h[g(-3)]$

19. $g[f(8)]$

20. $h[f(20)]$

21. $[f \circ (h \circ g)](-1)$

22. $[f \circ (g \circ h)](4)$

23. BUSINESS The function $f(x) = 1000 - 0.01x^2$ models the manufacturing cost per item when x items are produced, and $g(x) = 150 - 0.001x^2$ models the service cost per item. Write a function $C(x)$ for the total manufacturing and service cost per item.

24. MEASUREMENT The formula $f = \dfrac{n}{12}$ converts inches n to feet f, and $m = \dfrac{f}{5280}$ converts feet to miles m. Write a composition of functions that converts inches to miles.

7-8 Practice

Inverse Functions and Relations

Find the inverse of each relation.

1. {(0, 3), (4, 2), (5, −6)}

2. {(−5, 1), (−5, −1), (−5, 8)}

3. {(−3, −7), (0, −1), (5, 9), (7, 13)}

4. {(8, −2), (10, 5), (12, 6), (14, 7)}

5. {(−5, −4), (1, 2), (3, 4), (7, 8)}

6. {(−3, 9), (−2, 4), (0, 0), (1, 1)}

Find the inverse of each function. Then graph the function and its inverse.

7. $f(x) = \frac{3}{4}x$

8. $g(x) = 3 + x$

9. $y = 3x − 2$

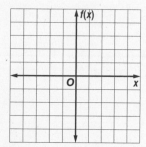
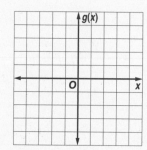
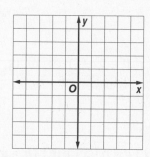

Determine whether each pair of functions are inverse functions.

10. $f(x) = x + 6$
 $g(x) = x − 6$

11. $f(x) = −4x + 1$
 $g(x) = \frac{1}{4}(1 − x)$

12. $g(x) = 13x − 13$
 $h(x) = \frac{1}{13}x − 1$

13. $f(x) = 2x$
 $g(x) = −2x$

14. $f(x) = \frac{6}{7}x$
 $g(x) = \frac{7}{6}x$

15. $g(x) = 2x − 8$
 $h(x) = \frac{1}{2}x + 4$

16. MEASUREMENT The points (63, 121), (71, 180), (67, 140), (65, 108), and (72, 165) give the weight in pounds as a function of height in inches for 5 students in a class. Give the points for these students that represent height as a function of weight.

REMODELING For Exercises 17 and 18, use the following information.

The Clearys are replacing the flooring in their 15 foot by 18 foot kitchen. The new flooring costs $17.99 per square yard. The formula $f(x) = 9x$ converts square yards to square feet.

17. Find the inverse $f^{-1}(x)$. What is the significance of $f^{-1}(x)$ for the Clearys?

18. What will the new flooring cost the Cleary's?

Glencoe Algebra 2

7-9 Practice

Square Root Functions and Inequalities

Graph each function. State the domain and range of each function.

1. $y = \sqrt{5x}$

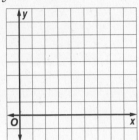

2. $y = -\sqrt{x - 1}$

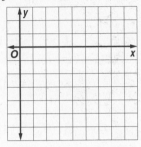

3. $y = 2\sqrt{x + 2}$

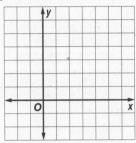

4. $y = \sqrt{3x - 4}$

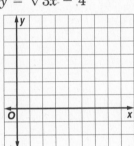

5. $y = \sqrt{x + 7} - 4$

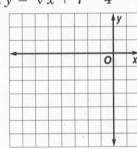

6. $y = 1 - \sqrt{2x + 3}$

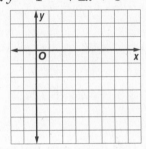

Graph each inequality.

7. $y \geq -\sqrt{6x}$

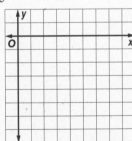

8. $y \leq \sqrt{x - 5} + 3$

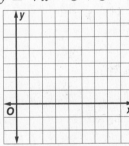

9. $y > -2\sqrt{3x + 2}$

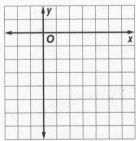

10. ROLLER COASTERS The velocity of a roller coaster as it moves down a hill is $v = \sqrt{v_0^2 + 64h}$, where v_0 is the initial velocity and h is the vertical drop in feet. If $v = 70$ feet per second and $v_0 = 8$ feet per second, find h.

11. WEIGHT Use the formula $d = \sqrt{\dfrac{3960^2 \, W_E}{W_s}} - 3960$, which relates distance from Earth d in miles to weight. If an astronaut's weight on Earth W_E is 148 pounds and in space W_s is 115 pounds, how far from Earth is the astronaut?

8-1 Practice

Midpoint and Distance Formulas

Find the midpoint of each line segment with endpoints at the given coordinates.

1. $(8, -3), (-6, -11)$ **2.** $(-14, 5), (10, 6)$

3. $(-7, -6), (1, -2)$ **4.** $(8, -2), (8, -8)$

5. $(9, -4), (1, -1)$ **6.** $(3, 3), (4, 9)$

7. $(4, -2), (3, -7)$ **8.** $(6, 7), (4, 4)$

9. $(-4, -2), (-8, 2)$ **10.** $(5, -2), (3, 7)$

11. $(-6, 3), (-5, -7)$ **12.** $(-9, -8), (8, 3)$

13. $(2.6, -4.7), (8.4, 2.5)$ **14.** $\left(-\dfrac{1}{3}, 6\right), \left(\dfrac{2}{3}, 4\right)$

15. $(-2.5, -4.2), (8.1, 4.2)$ **16.** $\left(\dfrac{1}{8}, \dfrac{1}{2}\right), \left(-\dfrac{5}{8}, -\dfrac{1}{2}\right)$

Find the distance between each pair of points with the given coordinates.

17. $(5, 2), (2, -2)$ **18.** $(-2, -4), (4, 4)$

19. $(-3, 8), (-1, -5)$ **20.** $(0, 1), (9, -6)$

21. $(-5, 6), (-6, 6)$ **22.** $(-3, 5), (12, -3)$

23. $(-2, -3), (9, 3)$ **24.** $(-9, -8), (-7, 8)$

25. $(9, 3), (9, -2)$ **26.** $(-1, -7), (0, 6)$

27. $(10, -3), (-2, -8)$ **28.** $(-0.5, -6), (1.5, 0)$

29. $\left(\dfrac{2}{5}, \dfrac{3}{5}\right), \left(1, \dfrac{7}{5}\right)$ **30.** $(-4\sqrt{2}, -\sqrt{5}), (-5\sqrt{2}, 4\sqrt{5})$

31. GEOMETRY Circle O has a diameter $\overline{AB}$. If A is at $(-6, -2)$ and B is at $(-3, 4)$, find the center of the circle and the length of its diameter.

32. GEOMETRY Find the perimeter of a triangle with vertices at $(1, -3), (-4, 9),$ and $(-2, 1)$.

8-2 Practice

Parabolas

Write each equation in standard form.

1. $y = 2x^2 - 12x + 19$

2. $y = \frac{1}{2}x^2 + 3x + \frac{1}{2}$

3. $y = -3x^2 - 12x - 7$

Identify the coordinates of the vertex and focus, the equations of the axis of symmetry and directrix, and the direction of opening of the parabola with the given equation. Then find the length of the latus rectum and graph the parabola.

4. $y = (x - 4)^2 + 3$

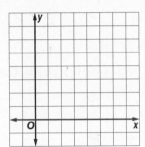

5. $x = -\frac{1}{3}y^2 + 1$

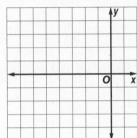

6. $x = 3(y + 1)^2 - 3$

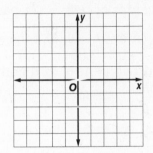

Write an equation for each parabola described below. Then draw the graph.

7. vertex $(0, -4)$,
   focus $\left(0, -3\frac{7}{8}\right)$

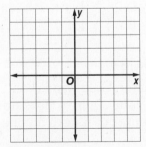

8. vertex $(-2, 1)$,
   directrix $x = -3$

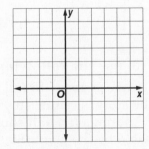

9. vertex $(1, 3)$,
   axis of symmetry $x = 1$,
   latus rectum: 2 units,
   $a < 0$

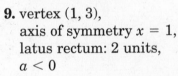
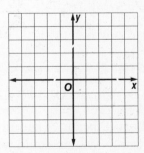

10. TELEVISION Write the equation in the form $y = ax^2$ for a satellite dish. Assume that the bottom of the upward-facing dish passes through $(0, 0)$ and that the distance from the bottom to the focus point is 8 inches.

8-3 Practice

Circles

Write an equation for the circle that satisfies each set of conditions.

1. center $(-4, 2)$, radius 8 units

2. center $(0, 0)$, radius 4 units

3. center $\left(-\dfrac{1}{4}, -\sqrt{3}\right)$, radius $5\sqrt{2}$ units

4. center $(2.5, 4.2)$, radius 0.9 unit

5. endpoints of a diameter at $(-2, -9)$ and $(0, -5)$

6. center at $(-9, -12)$, passes through $(-4, -5)$

7. center at $(-6, 5)$, tangent to x-axis

Find the center and radius of the circle with the given equation. Then graph the circle.

8. $(x + 3)^2 + y^2 = 16$

9. $3x^2 + 3y^2 = 12$

10. $x^2 + y^2 + 2x + 6y = 26$

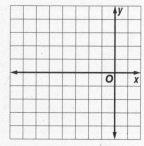

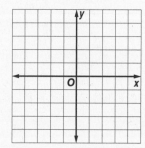

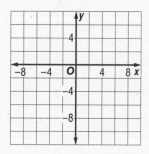

11. $(x - 1)^2 + y^2 + 4y = 12$

12. $x^2 - 6x + y^2 = 0$

13. $x^2 + y^2 + 2x + 6y = -1$

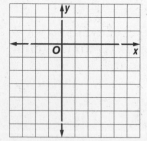

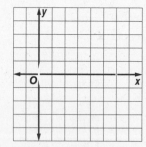

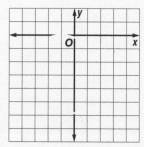

WEATHER For Exercises 14 and 15, use the following information.

On average, the circular eye of a hurricane is about 15 miles in diameter. Gale winds can affect an area up to 300 miles from the storm's center. In 1992, Hurricane Andrew devastated southern Florida. A satellite photo of Andrew's landfall showed the center of its eye on one coordinate system could be approximated by the point (80, 26).

14. Write an equation to represent a possible boundary of Andrew's eye.

15. Write an equation to represent a possible boundary of the area affected by gale winds.

8-4 Practice

Ellipses

Write an equation for each ellipse.

1.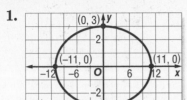

2.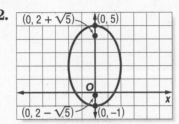

3.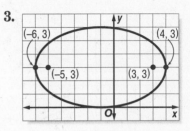

Write an equation for the ellipse that satisfies each set of conditions.

4. endpoints of major axis at $(-9, 0)$ and $(9, 0)$, endpoints of minor axis at $(0, 3)$ and $(0, -3)$

5. endpoints of major axis at $(4, 2)$ and $(4, -8)$, endpoints of minor axis at $(1, -3)$ and $(7, -3)$

6. major axis 20 units long and parallel to x-axis, minor axis 10 units long, center at $(2, 1)$

7. major axis 10 units long, minor axis 6 units long and parallel to x-axis, center at $(2, -4)$

8. major axis 16 units long, center at $(0, 0)$, foci at $(0, 2\sqrt{15})$ and $(0, -2\sqrt{15})$

9. endpoints of minor axis at $(0, 2)$ and $(0, -2)$, foci at $(-4, 0)$ and $(4, 0)$

Find the coordinates of the center and foci and the lengths of the major and minor axes for the ellipse with the given equation. Then graph the ellipse.

10. $\dfrac{y^2}{16} + \dfrac{x^2}{9} = 1$

11. $\dfrac{(y-1)^2}{36} + \dfrac{(x-3)^2}{1} = 1$

12. $\dfrac{(x+4)^2}{49} + \dfrac{(y+3)^2}{25} = 1$

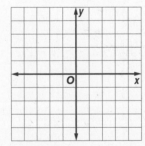

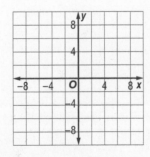

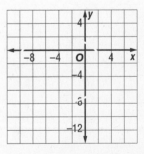

13. **SPORTS** An ice skater traces two congruent ellipses to form a figure eight. Assume that the center of the first loop is at the origin, with the second loop to its right. Write an equation to model the first loop if its major axis (along the x-axis) is 12 feet long and its minor axis is 6 feet long. Write another equation to model the second loop.

8-5 Practice

Hyperbolas

Write an equation for each hyperbola.

1.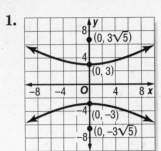

2.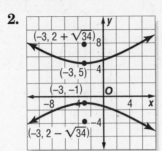

3.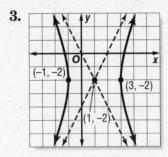

Write an equation for the hyperbola that satisfies each set of conditions.

4. vertices $(0, 7)$ and $(0, -7)$, conjugate axis of length 18 units

5. vertices $(1, -1)$ and $(1, -9)$, conjugate axis of length 6 units

6. vertices $(-5, 0)$ and $(5, 0)$, foci $\left(\pm\sqrt{26}, 0\right)$

7. vertices $(1, 1)$ and $(1, -3)$, foci $\left(1, -1 \pm \sqrt{5}\right)$

Find the coordinates of the vertices and foci and the equations of the asymptotes for the hyperbola with the given equation. Then graph the hyperbola.

8. $\dfrac{y^2}{16} - \dfrac{x^2}{4} = 1$

9. $\dfrac{(y-2)^2}{1} - \dfrac{(x-1)^2}{4} = 1$

10. $\dfrac{(y+2)^2}{4} - \dfrac{(x-3)^2}{4} = 1$

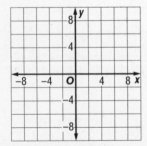

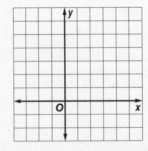

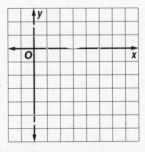

11. ASTRONOMY Astronomers use special X-ray telescopes to observe the sources of celestial X rays. Some X-ray telescopes are fitted with a metal mirror in the shape of a hyperbola, which reflects the X rays to a focus. Suppose the vertices of such a mirror are located at $(-3, 0)$ and $(3, 0)$, and one focus is located at $(5, 0)$. Write an equation that models the hyperbola formed by the mirror.

8-6 Practice

Conic Sections

Write each equation in standard form. State whether the graph of the equation is a *parabola*, *circle*, *ellipse*, or *hyperbola*. Then graph the equation.

1. $y^2 = -3x$

2. $x^2 + y^2 + 6x = 7$

3. $5x^2 - 6y^2 - 30x - 12y = -9$

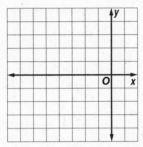
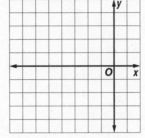
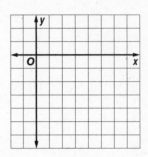

4. $196y^2 = 1225 - 100x^2$

5. $3x^2 = 9 - 3y^2 - 6y$

6. $9x^2 + y^2 + 54x - 6y = -81$

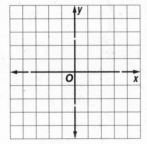
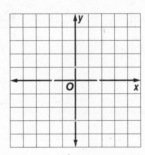
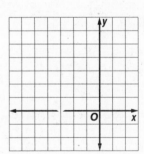

Without writing the equation in standard form, state whether the graph of each equation is a *parabola*, *circle*, *ellipse*, or *hyperbola*.

7. $6x^2 + 6y^2 = 36$

8. $4x^2 - y^2 = 16$

9. $9x^2 + 16y^2 - 64y - 80 = 0$

10. $5x^2 + 5y^2 - 45 = 0$

11. $x^2 + 2x = y$

12. $4y^2 - 36x^2 + 4x - 144 = 0$

13. ASTRONOMY A satellite travels in an hyperbolic orbit. It reaches the vertex of its orbit at $(5, 0)$ and then travels along a path that gets closer and closer to the line $y = \frac{2}{5}x$.

Write an equation that describes the path of the satellite if the center of its hyperbolic orbit is at $(0, 0)$.

8-7 Practice

Solving Quadratic Systems

Find the exact solution(s) of each system of equations.

1. $(x - 2)^2 + y^2 = 5$
$x - y = 1$

2. $x = 2(y + 1)^2 - 6$
$x + y = 3$

3. $y^2 - 3x^2 = 6$
$y = 2x - 1$

4. $x^2 + 2y^2 = 1$
$y = -x + 1$

5. $4y^2 - 9x^2 = 36$
$4x^2 - 9y^2 = 36$

6. $y = x^2 - 3$
$x^2 + y^2 = 9$

7. $x^2 + y^2 = 25$
$4y = 3x$

8. $y^2 = 10 - 6x^2$
$4y^2 = 40 - 2x^2$

9. $x^2 + y^2 = 25$
$x = 3y - 5$

10. $4x^2 + 9y^2 = 36$
$2x^2 - 9y^2 = 18$

11. $x = -(y - 3)^2 + 2$
$x = (y - 3)^2 + 3$

12. $\dfrac{x^2}{9} - \dfrac{y^2}{16} = 1$
$x^2 + y^2 = 9$

13. $25x^2 + 4y^2 = 100$
$x = -\dfrac{5}{2}$

14. $x^2 + y^2 = 4$
$\dfrac{x^2}{4} + \dfrac{y^2}{8} = 1$

15. $x^2 - y^2 = 3$
$y^2 - x^2 = 3$

16. $\dfrac{x^2}{7} + \dfrac{y^2}{7} = 1$
$3x^2 - y^2 = 9$

17. $x + 2y = 3$
$x^2 + y^2 = 9$

18. $x^2 + y^2 = 64$
$x^2 - y^2 = 8$

Solve each system of inequalities by graphing.

19. $y \geq x^2$
$y > -x + 2$

20. $x^2 + y^2 < 36$
$x^2 + y^2 \geq 16$

21. $\dfrac{(y - 3)^2}{16} + \dfrac{(x + 2)^2}{4} \leq 1$
$(x + 1)^2 + (y - 2)^2 \leq 4$

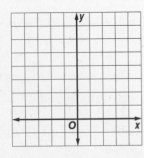

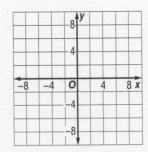

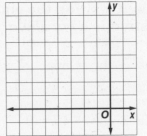

22. GEOMETRY The top of an iron gate is shaped like half an ellipse with two congruent segments from the center of the ellipse to the ellipse as shown. Assume that the center of the ellipse is at (0, 0). If the ellipse can be modeled by the equation $x^2 + 4y^2 = 4$ for $y \geq 0$ and the two congruent segments can be modeled by $y = \dfrac{\sqrt{3}}{2}x$ and $y = -\dfrac{\sqrt{3}}{2}x$, what are the coordinates of points A and B?

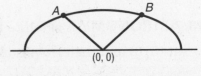

9-1 Practice

Multiplying and Dividing Rational Expressions

Simplify each expression.

1. $\dfrac{9a^2b^3}{27a^4b^4c}$

2. $\dfrac{(2m^3n^2)^3}{-18m^5n^4}$

3. $\dfrac{10y^2 + 15y}{35y^2 - 5y}$

4. $\dfrac{2k^2 - k - 15}{k^2 - 9}$

5. $\dfrac{25 - v^2}{3v^2 - 13v - 10}$

6. $\dfrac{x^4 + x^3 - 2x^2}{x^4 - x^3}$

7. $\dfrac{-2u^3y}{15xz^5} \cdot \dfrac{25x^3}{14u^2y^2}$

8. $\dfrac{a + y}{6} \cdot \dfrac{4}{y + a}$

9. $\dfrac{n^5}{n - 6} \cdot \dfrac{n^2 - 6n}{n^8}$

10. $\dfrac{a - y}{w + n} \cdot \dfrac{w^2 - n^2}{y - a}$

11. $\dfrac{x^2 - 5x - 24}{6x + 2x^2} \cdot \dfrac{5x^2}{8 - x}$

12. $\dfrac{x - 5}{10x - 2} \cdot \dfrac{25x^2 - 1}{x^2 - 10x + 25}$

13. $\dfrac{a^5y^3}{wy^7} \div \dfrac{a^3w^2}{w^5y^2}$

14. $\left(\dfrac{2xy}{w^2}\right)^3 \div \dfrac{24x^2}{w^5}$

15. $\dfrac{x + y}{6} \div \dfrac{x^2 - y^2}{3}$

16. $\dfrac{3x + 6}{x^2 - 9} \div \dfrac{6x^2 + 12x}{4x + 12}$

17. $\dfrac{2s^2 - 7s - 15}{(s + 4)^2} \div \dfrac{s^2 - 10s + 25}{s + 4}$

18. $\dfrac{9 - a^2}{a^2 + 5a + 6} \div \dfrac{2a - 6}{5a + 10}$

19. $\dfrac{\frac{2x + 1}{x}}{\frac{4 - x}{x}}$

20. $\dfrac{\frac{x^2 - 9}{4}}{\frac{3 - x}{8}}$

21. $\dfrac{\frac{x^3 + 2^3}{x^2 - 2x}}{\frac{(x + 2)^3}{x^2 + 4x + 4}}$

22. **GEOMETRY** A right triangle with an area of $x^2 - 4$ square units has a leg that measures $2x + 4$ units. Determine the length of the other leg of the triangle.

23. **GEOMETRY** A rectangular pyramid has a base area of $\dfrac{x^2 + 3x - 10}{2x}$ square centimeters and a height of $\dfrac{x^2 - 3x}{x^2 - 5x + 6}$ centimeters. Write a rational expression to describe the volume of the rectangular pyramid.

9-2 Practice

Adding and Subtracting Rational Expressions

Find the LCM of each set of polynomials.

1. x^2y, xy^3

2. a^2b^3c, abc^4

3. $x + 1, x + 3$

4. $g - 1, g^2 + 3g - 4$

5. $2r + 2, r^2 + r, r + 1$

6. $3, 4w + 2, 4w^2 - 1$

7. $x^2 + 2x - 8, x + 4$

8. $x^2 - x - 6, x^2 + 6x + 8$

9. $d^2 + 6d + 9, 2(d^2 - 9)$

Simplify each expression.

10. $\dfrac{5}{6ab} - \dfrac{7}{8a}$

11. $\dfrac{5}{12x^4y} - \dfrac{1}{5x^2y^3}$

12. $\dfrac{1}{6c^2d} + \dfrac{3}{4cd^3}$

13. $\dfrac{4m}{3mn} + 2$

14. $2x - 5 - \dfrac{x - 8}{x + 4}$

15. $\dfrac{4}{a - 3} + \dfrac{9}{a - 5}$

16. $\dfrac{16}{x^2 - 16} + \dfrac{2}{x + 4}$

17. $\dfrac{2 - 5m}{m - 9} + \dfrac{4m - 5}{9 - m}$

18. $\dfrac{y - 5}{y^2 - 3y - 10} + \dfrac{y}{y^2 + y - 2}$

19. $\dfrac{5}{2x - 12} - \dfrac{20}{x^2 - 4x - 12}$

20. $\dfrac{2p - 3}{p^2 - 5p + 6} - \dfrac{5}{p^2 - 9}$

21. $\dfrac{1}{5n} - \dfrac{3}{4} + \dfrac{7}{10n}$

22. $\dfrac{2a}{a - 3} - \dfrac{2a}{a + 3} + \dfrac{36}{a^2 - 9}$

23. $\dfrac{\dfrac{2}{x - y} + \dfrac{1}{x + y}}{\dfrac{1}{x - y}}$

24. $\dfrac{\dfrac{r + 6}{r} - \dfrac{1}{r + 2}}{\dfrac{r^2 + 4r + 3}{r^2 + 2r}}$

25. GEOMETRY The expressions $\dfrac{5x}{2}, \dfrac{20}{x + 4}$, and $\dfrac{10}{x - 4}$ represent the lengths of the sides of a triangle. Write a simplified expression for the perimeter of the triangle.

26. KAYAKING Mai is kayaking on a river that has a current of 2 miles per hour. If r represents her rate in calm water, then $r + 2$ represents her rate with the current, and $r - 2$ represents her rate against the current. Mai kayaks 2 miles downstream and then back to her starting point. Use the formula for time, $t = \dfrac{d}{r}$, where d is the distance, to write a simplified expression for the total time it takes Mai to complete the trip.

9-3 **Practice**

Graphing Rational Functions

Determine the equations of any vertical asymptotes and the values of x for any holes in the graph of each rational function.

1. $f(x) = \dfrac{6}{x^2 + 3x - 10}$

2. $f(x) = \dfrac{x - 7}{x^2 - 10x + 21}$

3. $f(x) = \dfrac{x - 2}{x^2 + 4x + 4}$

4. $f(x) = \dfrac{x^2 - 100}{x + 10}$

5. $f(x) = \dfrac{x^2 - 2x - 24}{x - 6}$

6. $f(x) = \dfrac{x^2 + 9x + 20}{x + 5}$

Graph each rational function.

7. $f(x) = \dfrac{-4}{x - 2}$

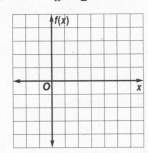

8. $f(x) = \dfrac{x - 3}{x - 2}$

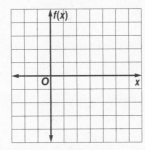

9. $f(x) = \dfrac{3x}{(x + 3)^2}$

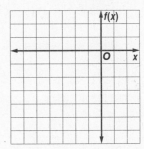

10. PAINTING Working alone, Tawa can give the shed a coat of paint in 6 hours. It takes her father x hours working alone to give the shed a coat of paint. The equation $f(x) = \dfrac{6 + x}{6x}$ describes the portion of the job Tawa and her father working together can complete in 1 hour. Graph $f(x) = \dfrac{6 + x}{6x}$ for $x \geq 0, y \geq 0$. If Tawa's father can complete the job in 4 hours alone, what portion of the job can they complete together in 1 hour?

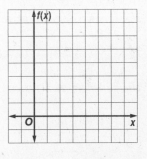

11. LIGHT The relationship between the illumination an object receives from a light source of I foot-candles and the square of the distance d in feet of the object from the source can be modeled by $I(d) = \dfrac{4500}{d^2}$. Graph the function $I(d) = \dfrac{4500}{d^2}$ for $0 \leq I \leq 80$ and $0 \leq d \leq 80$. What is the illumination in foot-candles that the object receives at a distance of 20 feet from the light source?

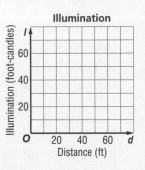

Illumination

Illumination (foot-candles)

Distance (ft)

9-4 Practice

Direct, Joint, and Inverse Variation

State whether each equation represents a _direct_, _joint_, or _inverse_ variation. Then name the constant of variation.

1. $u = 8wz$ **2.** $p = 4s$ **3.** $L = \dfrac{5}{k}$ **4.** $xy = 4.5$

5. $\dfrac{C}{d} = \pi$ **6.** $2d = mn$ **7.** $\dfrac{1.25}{g} = h$ **8.** $y = \dfrac{3}{4x}$

Find each value.

9. If y varies directly as x and $y = 8$ when $x = 2$, find y when $x = 6$.

10. If y varies directly as x and $y = -16$ when $x = 6$, find x when $y = -4$.

11. If y varies directly as x and $y = 132$ when $x = 11$, find y when $x = 33$.

12. If y varies directly as x and $y = 7$ when $x = 1.5$, find y when $x = 4$.

13. If y varies jointly as x and z and $y = 24$ when $x = 2$ and $z = 1$, find y when $x = 12$ and $z = 2$.

14. If y varies jointly as x and z and $y = 60$ when $x = 3$ and $z = 4$, find y when $x = 6$ and $z = 8$.

15. If y varies jointly as x and z and $y = 12$ when $x = -2$ and $z = 3$, find y when $x = 4$ and $z = -1$.

16. If y varies inversely as x and $y = 16$ when $x = 4$, find y when $x = 3$.

17. If y varies inversely as x and $y = 3$ when $x = 5$, find x when $y = 2.5$.

18. If y varies inversely as x and $y = -18$ when $x = 6$, find y when $x = 5$.

19. If y varies directly as x and $y = 5$ when $x = 0.4$, find x when $y = 37.5$.

20. GASES The volume V of a gas varies inversely as its pressure P. If $V = 80$ cubic centimeters when $P = 2000$ millimeters of mercury, find V when $P = 320$ millimeters of mercury.

21. SPRINGS The length S that a spring will stretch varies directly with the weight F that is attached to the spring. If a spring stretches 20 inches with 25 pounds attached, how far will it stretch with 15 pounds attached?

22. GEOMETRY The area A of a trapezoid varies jointly as its height and the sum of its bases. If the area is 480 square meters when the height is 20 meters and the bases are 28 meters and 20 meters, what is the area of a trapezoid when its height is 8 meters and its bases are 10 meters and 15 meters?

9-5 Practice

Classes of Functions

Identify the type of function represented by each graph.

1.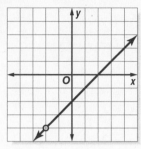

2.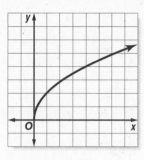

3.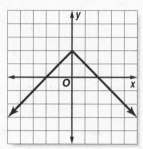

Match each graph with an equation below.

A. $y = |2x + 1|$ **B.** $y = [\![2x + 1]\!]$ **C.** $y = \dfrac{x - 3}{2}$ **D.** $y = \sqrt{-x}$

4.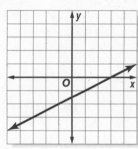

5.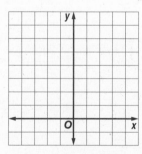

6.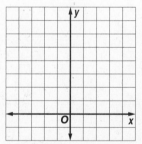

Identify the type of function represented by each equation. Then graph the equation.

7. $y = -3$

8. $y = 2x^2 + 1$

9. $y = \dfrac{x^2 + 5x + 6}{x + 2}$

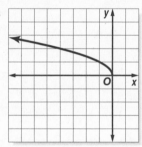

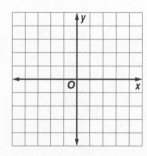

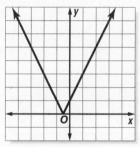

10. BUSINESS A startup company uses the function $P = 1.3x^2 + 3x - 7$ to predict its profit or loss during its first 7 years of operation. Describe the shape of the graph of the function.

11. PARKING A parking lot charges \$10 to park for the first day or part of a day. After that, it charges an additional \$8 per day or part of a day. Describe the graph and find the cost of parking for $6\frac{1}{2}$ days.

9-6 Practice

Solving Rational Equations and Inequalities

Solve each equation or inequality. Check your solutions.

1. $\dfrac{12}{x} + \dfrac{3}{4} = \dfrac{3}{2}$

2. $\dfrac{x}{x-1} - 1 = \dfrac{x}{2}$

3. $\dfrac{p+10}{p^2-2} = \dfrac{4}{p}$

4. $\dfrac{s}{s+2} + s = \dfrac{5s+8}{s+2}$

5. $\dfrac{5}{y-5} = \dfrac{y}{y-5} - 1$

6. $\dfrac{1}{3x-2} + \dfrac{5}{x} = 0$

7. $\dfrac{5}{t} < \dfrac{9}{2t+1}$

8. $\dfrac{1}{2h} + \dfrac{5}{h} = \dfrac{3}{h-1}$

9. $\dfrac{4}{w-2} = \dfrac{-1}{w+3}$

10. $5 - \dfrac{3}{a} < \dfrac{7}{a}$

11. $\dfrac{4}{5x} + \dfrac{1}{10} < \dfrac{3}{2x}$

12. $8 + \dfrac{3}{y} > \dfrac{19}{y}$

13. $\dfrac{4}{p} + \dfrac{1}{3p} < \dfrac{1}{5}$

14. $\dfrac{6}{x-1} = \dfrac{4}{x-2} + \dfrac{2}{x+1}$

15. $g + \dfrac{g}{g-2} = \dfrac{2}{g-2}$

16. $b + \dfrac{2b}{b-1} = 1 - \dfrac{b-3}{b-1}$

17. $2 = \dfrac{x+2}{x-3} + \dfrac{x-2}{x-6}$

18. $5 - \dfrac{3d+2}{d-1} = \dfrac{2d-4}{d+2}$

19. $\dfrac{1}{n+2} + \dfrac{1}{n-2} = \dfrac{3}{n^2-4}$

20. $\dfrac{c+1}{c-3} = 4 - \dfrac{12}{c^2-2c-3}$

21. $\dfrac{3}{k-3} + \dfrac{4}{k-4} = \dfrac{25}{k^2-7k+12}$

22. $\dfrac{4v}{v-1} - \dfrac{5v}{v-2} = \dfrac{2}{v^2-3v+2}$

23. $\dfrac{y}{y+2} + \dfrac{7}{y-5} = \dfrac{14}{y^2-3y-10}$

24. $\dfrac{x^2+4}{x^2-4} + \dfrac{x}{2-x} = \dfrac{2}{x+2}$

25. $\dfrac{r}{r+4} + \dfrac{4}{r-4} = \dfrac{r^2+16}{r^2-16}$

26. $3 = \dfrac{6a-1}{2a+7} + \dfrac{22}{a+5}$

27. **BASKETBALL** Kiana has made 9 of 19 free throws so far this season. Her goal is to make 60% of her free throws. If Kiana makes her next x free throws in a row, the function $f(x) = \dfrac{9+x}{19+x}$ represents Kiana's new ratio of free throws made. How many successful free throws in a row will raise Kiana's percent made to 60%?

28. **OPTICS** The lens equation $\dfrac{1}{p} + \dfrac{1}{q} = \dfrac{1}{f}$ relates the distance p of an object from a lens, the distance q of the image of the object from the lens, and the focal length f of the lens. What is the distance of an object from a lens if the image of the object is 5 centimeters from the lens and the focal length of the lens is 4 centimeters?

10-1 **Practice**

Exponential Functions

Sketch the graph of each function. Then state the function's domain and range.

1. $y = 1.5(2)^x$

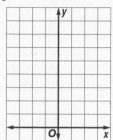

2. $y = 4(3)^x$

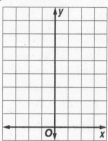

3. $y = 3(0.5)^x$

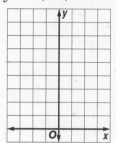

Determine whether each function represents exponential *growth* or *decay*.

4. $y = 5(0.6)^x$ **5.** $y = 0.1(2)^x$ **6.** $y = 5 \cdot 4^{-x}$

Write an exponential function whose graph passes through the given points.

7. $(0, 1)$ and $(-1, 4)$ **8.** $(0, 2)$ and $(1, 10)$ **9.** $(0, -3)$ and $(1, -1.5)$

10. $(0, 0.8)$ and $(1, 1.6)$ **11.** $(0, -0.4)$ and $(2, -10)$ **12.** $(0, \pi)$ and $(3, 8\pi)$

Simplify each expression.

13. $\left(2^{\sqrt{2}}\right)^{\sqrt{8}}$ **14.** $\left(n^{\sqrt{3}}\right)^{\sqrt{75}}$ **15.** $y^{\sqrt{6}} \cdot y^{5\sqrt{6}}$

16. $13^{\sqrt{6}} \cdot 13^{\sqrt{24}}$ **17.** $n^3 \div n^{\pi}$ **18.** $125^{\sqrt{11}} \div 5^{\sqrt{11}}$

Solve each equation or inequality. Check your solution.

19. $3^{3x-5} > 81$ **20.** $7^{6x} = 7^{2x-20}$ **21.** $3^{6n-5} < 9^{4n-3}$

22. $9^{2x-1} = 27^{x+4}$ **23.** $2^{3n-1} \geq \left(\dfrac{1}{8}\right)^n$ **24.** $16^{4n-1} = 128^{2n+1}$

BIOLOGY For Exercises 25 and 26, use the following information.

The initial number of bacteria in a culture is 12,000. The number after 3 days is 96,000.

25. Write an exponential function to model the population y of bacteria after x days.

26. How many bacteria are there after 6 days?

27. EDUCATION A college with a graduating class of 4000 students in the year 2002 predicts that it will have a graduating class of 4862 in 4 years. Write an exponential function to model the number of students y in the graduating class t years after 2002.

10-2 Practice

Logarithms and Logarithmic Functions

Write each equation in logarithmic form.

1. $5^3 = 125$

2. $7^0 = 1$

3. $3^4 = 81$

4. $3^{-4} = \dfrac{1}{81}$

5. $\left(\dfrac{1}{4}\right)^3 = \dfrac{1}{64}$

6. $7776^{\frac{1}{5}} = 6$

Write each equation in exponential form.

7. $\log_6 216 = 3$

8. $\log_2 64 = 6$

9. $\log_3 \dfrac{1}{81} = -4$

10. $\log_{10} 0.00001 = -5$

11. $\log_{25} 5 = \dfrac{1}{2}$

12. $\log_{32} 8 = \dfrac{3}{5}$

Evaluate each expression.

13. $\log_3 81$

14. $\log_{10} 0.0001$

15. $\log_2 \dfrac{1}{16}$

16. $\log_{\frac{1}{3}} 27$

17. $\log_9 1$

18. $\log_8 4$

19. $\log_7 \dfrac{1}{49}$

20. $\log_6 6^4$

21. $\log_3 \dfrac{1}{3}$

22. $\log_4 \dfrac{1}{256}$

23. $\log_9 9^{(n+1)}$

24. $2^{\log_2 32}$

Solve each equation or inequality. Check your solutions.

25. $\log_{10} n = -3$

26. $\log_4 x > 3$

27. $\log_4 x = \dfrac{3}{2}$

28. $\log_{\frac{1}{5}} x = -3$

29. $\log_7 q < 0$

30. $\log_6 (2y + 8) \geq 2$

31. $\log_y 16 = -4$

32. $\log_n \dfrac{1}{8} = -3$

33. $\log_b 1024 = 5$

34. $\log_8 (3x + 7) < \log_8 (7x + 4)$ **35.** $\log_7 (8x + 20) = \log_7 (x + 6)$ **36.** $\log_3 (x^2 - 2) = \log_3 x$

37. SOUND Sounds that reach levels of 130 decibels or more are painful to humans. What is the relative intensity of 130 decibels?

38. INVESTING Maria invests \$1000 in a savings account that pays 8% interest compounded annually. The value of the account A at the end of five years can be determined from the equation $\log A = \log[1000(1 + 0.08)^5]$. Find the value of A to the nearest dollar.

10-3 Practice

Properties of Logarithms

Use $\log_{10} 5 \approx 0.6990$ and $\log_{10} 7 \approx 0.8451$ to approximate the value of each expression.

1. $\log_{10} 35$ **2.** $\log_{10} 25$ **3.** $\log_{10} \frac{7}{5}$ **4.** $\log_{10} \frac{5}{7}$

5. $\log_{10} 245$ **6.** $\log_{10} 175$ **7.** $\log_{10} 0.2$ **8.** $\log_{10} \frac{25}{7}$

Solve each equation. Check your solutions.

9. $\log_7 n = \frac{2}{3} \log_7 8$

10. $\log_{10} u = \frac{3}{2} \log_{10} 4$

11. $\log_6 x + \log_6 9 = \log_6 54$

12. $\log_8 48 - \log_8 w = \log_8 4$

13. $\log_9 (3u + 14) - \log_9 5 = \log_9 2u$

14. $4 \log_2 x + \log_2 5 = \log_2 405$

15. $\log_3 y = -\log_3 16 + \frac{1}{3} \log_3 64$

16. $\log_2 d = 5 \log_2 2 - \log_2 8$

17. $\log_{10} (3m - 5) + \log_{10} m = \log_{10} 2$

18. $\log_{10} (b + 3) + \log_{10} b = \log_{10} 4$

19. $\log_8 (t + 10) - \log_8 (t - 1) = \log_8 12$

20. $\log_3 (a + 3) + \log_3 (a + 2) = \log_3 6$

21. $\log_{10} (r + 4) - \log_{10} r = \log_{10} (r + 1)$

22. $\log_4 (x^2 - 4) - \log_4 (x + 2) = \log_4 1$

23. $\log_{10} 4 + \log_{10} w = 2$

24. $\log_8 (n - 3) + \log_8 (n + 4) = 1$

25. $3 \log_5 (x^2 + 9) - 6 = 0$

26. $\log_{16} (9x + 5) - \log_{16} (x^2 - 1) = \frac{1}{2}$

27. $\log_6 (2x - 5) + 1 = \log_6 (7x + 10)$

28. $\log_2 (5y + 2) - 1 = \log_2 (1 - 2y)$

29. $\log_{10} (c^2 - 1) - 2 = \log_{10} (c + 1)$

30. $\log_7 x + 2 \log_7 x - \log_7 3 = \log_7 72$

31. SOUND The loudness L of a sound in decibels is given by $L = 10 \log_{10} R$, where R is the sound's relative intensity. If the intensity of a certain sound is tripled, by how many decibels does the sound increase?

32. EARTHQUAKES An earthquake rated at 3.5 on the Richter scale is felt by many people, and an earthquake rated at 4.5 may cause local damage. The Richter scale magnitude reading m is given by $m = \log_{10} x$, where x represents the amplitude of the seismic wave causing ground motion. How many times greater is the amplitude of an earthquake that measures 4.5 on the Richter scale than one that measures 3.5?

10-4 Practice

Common Logarithms

Use a calculator to evaluate each expression to four decimal places.

1. log 101

2. log 2.2

3. log 0.05

Use the formula pH = −log[H+] to find the pH of each substance given its concentration of hydrogen ions.

4. milk: $[H+] = 2.51 \times 10^{-7}$ mole per liter

5. acid rain: $[H+] = 2.51 \times 10^{-6}$ mole per liter

6. black coffee: $[H+] = 1.0 \times 10^{-5}$ mole per liter

7. milk of magnesia: $[H+] = 3.16 \times 10^{-11}$ mole per liter

Solve each equation or inequality. Round to four decimal places.

8. $2^x < 25$

9. $5^a = 120$

10. $6^z = 45.6$

11. $9^m \geq 100$

12. $3.5^x = 47.9$

13. $8.2^y = 64.5$

14. $2^{b+1} \leq 7.31$

15. $4^{2x} = 27$

16. $2^{a-4} = 82.1$

17. $9^{z-2} > 38$

18. $5^{w+3} = 17$

19. $30^{x^2} = 50$

20. $5^{x^2-3} = 72$

21. $4^{2x} = 9^{x+1}$

22. $2^{n+1} = 5^{2n-1}$

Express each logarithm in terms of common logarithms. Then approximate its value to four decimal places.

23. $\log_5 12$

24. $\log_8 32$

25. $\log_{11} 9$

26. $\log_2 18$

27. $\log_9 6$

28. $\log_7 \sqrt{8}$

29. HORTICULTURE Siberian irises flourish when the concentration of hydrogen ions $[H+]$ in the soil is not less than 1.58×10^{-8} mole per liter. What is the pH of the soil in which these irises will flourish?

30. ACIDITY The pH of vinegar is 2.9 and the pH of milk is 6.6. How many times greater is the hydrogen ion concentration of vinegar than of milk?

31. BIOLOGY There are initially 1000 bacteria in a culture. The number of bacteria doubles each hour. The number of bacteria N present after t hours is $N = 1000(2)^t$. How long will it take the culture to increase to 50,000 bacteria?

32. SOUND An equation for loudness L in decibels is given by $L = 10 \log R$, where R is the sound's relative intensity. An air-raid siren can reach 150 decibels and jet engine noise can reach 120 decibels. How many times greater is the relative intensity of the air-raid siren than that of the jet engine noise?

10-5 Practice

Base e and Natural Logarithms

Use a calculator to evaluate each expression to four decimal places.

1. $e^{1.5}$ **2.** $\ln 8$ **3.** $\ln 3.2$ **4.** $e^{-0.6}$

5. $e^{4.2}$ **6.** $\ln 1$ **7.** $e^{-2.5}$ **8.** $\ln 0.037$

Write an equivalent exponential or logarithmic equation.

9. $\ln 50 = x$ **10.** $\ln 36 = 2x$ **11.** $\ln 6 \approx 1.7918$ **12.** $\ln 9.3 \approx 2.2300$

13. $e^x = 8$ **14.** $e^5 = 10x$ **15.** $e^{-x} = 4$ **16.** $e^2 = x + 1$

Evaluate each expression.

17. $e^{\ln 12}$ **18.** $e^{\ln 3x}$ **19.** $\ln e^{-1}$ **20.** $\ln e^{-2y}$

Solve each equation or inequality.

21. $e^x < 9$ **22.** $e^{-x} = 31$ **23.** $e^x = 1.1$ **24.** $e^x = 5.8$

25. $2e^x - 3 = 1$ **26.** $5e^x + 1 \geq 7$ **27.** $4 + e^x = 19$ **28.** $-3e^x + 10 < 8$

29. $e^{3x} = 8$ **30.** $e^{-4x} = 5$ **31.** $e^{0.5x} = 6$ **32.** $2e^{5x} = 24$

33. $e^{2x} + 1 = 55$ **34.** $e^{3x} - 5 = 32$ **35.** $9 + e^{2x} = 10$ **36.** $e^{-3x} + 7 \geq 15$

37. $\ln 4x = 3$ **38.** $\ln (-2x) = 7$ **39.** $\ln 2.5x = 10$ **40.** $\ln (x - 6) = 1$

41. $\ln (x + 2) = 3$ **42.** $\ln (x + 3) = 5$ **43.** $\ln 3x + \ln 2x = 9$ **44.** $\ln 5x + \ln x = 7$

INVESTING For Exercises 45 and 46, use the formula for continuously compounded interest, $A = Pe^{rt}$, where P is the principal, r is the annual interest rate, and t is the time in years.

45. If Sarita deposits \$1000 in an account paying 3.4% annual interest compounded continuously, what is the balance in the account after 5 years?

46. How long will it take the balance in Sarita's account to reach \$2000?

47. RADIOACTIVE DECAY The amount of a radioactive substance y that remains after t years is given by the equation $y = ae^{kt}$, where a is the initial amount present and k is the decay constant for the radioactive substance. If $a = 100$, $y = 50$, and $k = -0.035$, find t.

10-6 **Practice**

Exponential Growth and Decay

Solve each problem.

1. **INVESTING** The formula $A = P\left(1 + \dfrac{r}{2}\right)^{2t}$ gives the value of an investment after t years in an account that earns an annual interest rate r compounded twice a year. Suppose \$500 is invested at 6% annual interest compounded twice a year. In how many years will the investment be worth \$1000?

2. **BACTERIA** How many hours will it take a culture of bacteria to increase from 20 to 2000 if the growth rate per hour is 85%?

3. **RADIOACTIVE DECAY** A radioactive substance has a half-life of 32 years. Find the constant k in the decay formula for the substance.

4. **DEPRECIATION** A piece of machinery valued at \$250,000 depreciates at a fixed rate of 12% per year. After how many years will the value have depreciated to \$100,000?

5. **INFLATION** For Dave to buy a new car comparably equipped to the one he bought years ago would cost \$12,500. Since Dave bought the car, the inflation rate for cars like his has been at an average annual rate of 5.1%. If Dave originally paid \$8400 for the car, how long ago did he buy it?

6. **RADIOACTIVE DECAY** Cobalt, an element used to make alloys, has several isotopes. One of these, cobalt-60, is radioactive and has a half-life of 5.7 years. Cobalt-60 is used to trace the path of nonradioactive substances in a system. What is the value of k for Cobalt-60?

7. **WHALES** Modern whales appeared 5–10 million years ago. The vertebrae of a whale discovered by paleontologists contain roughly 0.25% as much carbon-14 as they would have contained when the whale was alive. How long ago did the whale die? Use $k = 0.00012$.

8. **POPULATION** The population of rabbits in an area is modeled by the growth equation $P(t) = 8e^{0.26t}$, where P is in thousands and t is in years. How long will it take for the population to reach 25,000?

9. **DEPRECIATION** A computer system depreciates at an average rate of 4% per month. If the value of the computer system was originally \$12,000, in how many months is it worth \$7350?

10. **BIOLOGY** In a laboratory, a culture increases from 30 to 195 organisms in 5 hours. What is the hourly growth rate in the growth formula $y = a(1 + r)^t$?

11-1 Practice

Arithmetic Sequences

Find the next four terms of each arithmetic sequence.

1. 5, 8, 11, ...

2. $-4, -6, -8, ...$

3. 100, 93, 86, ...

4. $-24, -19, -14, ...$

5. $\frac{7}{2}, 6, \frac{17}{2}, 11, ...$

6. 4.8, 4.1, 3.4, ...

Find the first five terms of each arithmetic sequence described.

7. $a_1 = 7, d = 7$

8. $a_1 = -8, d = 2$

9. $a_1 = -12, d = -4$

10. $a_1 = \frac{1}{2}, d = \frac{1}{2}$

11. $a_1 = -\frac{5}{6}, d = -\frac{1}{3}$

12. $a_1 = 10.2, d = -5.8$

Find the indicated term of each arithmetic sequence.

13. $a_1 = 5, d = 3, n = 10$

14. $a_1 = 9, d = 3, n = 29$

15. a_{18} for $-6, -7, -8, ...$

16. a_{37} for 124, 119, 114, ...

17. $a_1 = \frac{9}{5}, d = -\frac{3}{5}, n = 10$

18. $a_1 = 14.25, d = 0.15, n = 31$

Complete the statement for each arithmetic sequence.

19. 166 is the __?__th term of 30, 34, 38, ...

20. 2 is the __?__th term of $\frac{3}{5}, \frac{4}{5}, 1, ...$

Write an equation for the nth term of each arithmetic sequence.

21. $-5, -3, -1, 1, ...$

22. $-8, -11, -14, -17, ...$

23. $1, -1, -3, -5, ...$

24. $-5, 3, 11, 19, ...$

Find the arithmetic means in each sequence.

25. $-5, \underline{\ ?\ }, \underline{\ ?\ }, \underline{\ ?\ }, 11$

26. 82, $\underline{\ ?\ }, \underline{\ ?\ }, \underline{\ ?\ }, 18$

27. EDUCATION Trevor Koba has opened an English Language School in Isehara, Japan. He began with 26 students. If he enrolls 3 new students each week, in how many weeks will he have 101 students?

28. SALARIES Yolanda interviewed for a job that promised her a starting salary of $32,000 with a $1250 raise at the end of each year. What will her salary be during her sixth year if she accepts the job?

11-2 Practice

Arithmetic Series

Find S_n for each arithmetic series described.

1. $a_1 = 16, a_n = 98, n = 13$

2. $a_1 = 3, a_n = 36, n = 12$

3. $a_1 = -5, a_n = -26, n = 8$

4. $a_1 = 5, n = 10, a_n = -13$

5. $a_1 = 6, n = 15, a_n = -22$

6. $a_1 = -20, n = 25, a_n = 148$

7. $a_1 = 13, d = -6, n = 21$

8. $a_1 = 5, d = 4, n = 11$

9. $a_1 = 5, d = 2, a_n = 33$

10. $a_1 = -121, d = 3, a_n = 5$

11. $d = 0.4, n = 10, a_n = 3.8$

12. $d = -\frac{2}{3}, n = 16, a_n = 44$

Find the sum of each arithmetic series.

13. $5 + 7 + 9 + 11 + \ldots + 27$

14. $-4 + 1 + 6 + 11 + \ldots + 91$

15. $13 + 20 + 27 + \ldots + 272$

16. $89 + 86 + 83 + 80 + \ldots + 20$

17. $\sum\limits_{n=1}^{4} (1 - 2n)$

18. $\sum\limits_{j=1}^{6} (5 + 3n)$

19. $\sum\limits_{n=1}^{5} (9 - 4n)$

20. $\sum\limits_{k=4}^{10} (2k + 1)$

21. $\sum\limits_{n=3}^{8} (5n - 10)$

22. $\sum\limits_{n=1}^{101} (4 - 4n)$

Find the first three terms of each arithmetic series described.

23. $a_1 = 14, a_n = -85, S_n = -1207$

24. $a_1 = 1, a_n = 19, S_n = 100$

25. $n = 16, a_n = 15, S_n = -120$

26. $n = 15, a_n = 5\frac{4}{5}, S_n = 45$

27. STACKING A health club rolls its towels and stacks them in layers on a shelf. Each layer of towels has one less towel than the layer below it. If there are 20 towels on the bottom layer and one towel on the top layer, how many towels are stacked on the shelf?

28. BUSINESS A merchant places \$1 in a jackpot on August 1, then draws the name of a regular customer. If the customer is present, he or she wins the \$1 in the jackpot. If the customer is not present, the merchant adds \$2 to the jackpot on August 2 and draws another name. Each day the merchant adds an amount equal to the day of the month. If the first person to win the jackpot wins \$496, on what day of the month was her or his name drawn?

11-3 Practice

Geometric Sequences

Find the next two terms of each geometric sequence.

1. $-15, -30, -60, \ldots$

2. $80, 40, 20, \ldots$

3. $90, 30, 10, \ldots$

4. $-1458, 486, -162, \ldots$

5. $\dfrac{1}{4}, \dfrac{3}{8}, \dfrac{9}{16}, \ldots$

6. $216, 144, 96, \ldots$

Find the first five terms of each geometric sequence described.

7. $a_1 = -1, r = -3$

8. $a_1 = 7, r = -4$

9. $a_1 = -\dfrac{1}{3}, r = 2$

10. $a_1 = 12, r = \dfrac{2}{3}$

Find the indicated term of each geometric sequence.

11. $a_1 = 5, r = 3, n = 6$

12. $a_1 = 20, r = -3, n = 6$

13. $a_1 = -4, r = -2, n = 10$

14. a_8 for $-\dfrac{1}{250}, -\dfrac{1}{50}, -\dfrac{1}{10}, \ldots$

15. a_{12} for $96, 48, 24, \ldots$

16. $a_1 = 8, r = \dfrac{1}{2}, n = 9$

17. $a_1 = -3125, r = -\dfrac{1}{5}, n = 9$

18. $a_1 = 3, r = \dfrac{1}{10}, n = 8$

Write an equation for the *n*th term of each geometric sequence.

19. $1, 4, 16, \ldots$

20. $-1, -5, -25, \ldots$

21. $1, \dfrac{1}{2}, \dfrac{1}{4}, \ldots$

22. $-3, -6, -12, \ldots$

23. $7, -14, 28, \ldots$

24. $-5, -30, -180, \ldots$

Find the geometric means in each sequence.

25. $3, \underline{\ ?\ }, \underline{\ ?\ }, \underline{\ ?\ }, 768$

26. $5, \underline{\ ?\ }, \underline{\ ?\ }, \underline{\ ?\ }, 1280$

27. $144, \underline{\ ?\ }, \underline{\ ?\ }, \underline{\ ?\ }, 9$

28. $37,500, \underline{\ ?\ }, \underline{\ ?\ }, \underline{\ ?\ }, \underline{\ ?\ }, -12$

29. **BIOLOGY** A culture initially contains 200 bacteria. If the number of bacteria doubles every 2 hours, how many bacteria will be in the culture at the end of 12 hours?

30. **LIGHT** If each foot of water in a lake screens out 60% of the light above, what percent of the light passes through 5 feet of water?

31. **INVESTING** Raul invests $1000 in a savings account that earns 5% interest compounded annually. How much money will he have in the account at the end of 5 years?

11-4 Practice

Geometric Series

Find S_n for each geometric series described.

1. $a_1 = 2, a_6 = 64, r = 2$

2. $a_1 = 160, a_6 = 5, r = \dfrac{1}{2}$

3. $a_1 = -3, a_n = -192, r = -2$

4. $a_1 = -81, a_n = -16, r = -\dfrac{2}{3}$

5. $a_1 = -3, a_n = 3072, r = -4$

6. $a_1 = 54, a_6 = \dfrac{2}{9}, r = \dfrac{1}{3}$

7. $a_1 = 5, r = 3, n = 9$

8. $a_1 = -6, r = -1, n = 21$

9. $a_1 = -6, r = -3, n = 7$

10. $a_1 = -9, r = \dfrac{2}{3}, n = 4$

11. $a_1 = \dfrac{1}{3}, r = 3, n = 10$

12. $a_1 = 16, r = -1.5, n = 6$

Find the sum of each geometric series.

13. $162 + 54 + 18 + \ldots$ to 6 terms

14. $2 + 4 + 8 + \ldots$ to 8 terms

15. $64 - 96 + 144 - \ldots$ to 7 terms

16. $\dfrac{1}{9} - \dfrac{1}{3} + 1 - \ldots$ to 6 terms

17. $\displaystyle\sum_{n=1}^{8} (-3)^{n-1}$

18. $\displaystyle\sum_{n=1}^{9} 5(-2)^{n-1}$

19. $\displaystyle\sum_{n=1}^{5} -1(4)^{n-1}$

20. $\displaystyle\sum_{n=1}^{6} \left(\dfrac{1}{2}\right)^{n-1}$

21. $\displaystyle\sum_{n=1}^{10} 2560\left(\dfrac{1}{2}\right)^{n-1}$

22. $\displaystyle\sum_{n=1}^{4} 9\left(\dfrac{2}{3}\right)^{n-1}$

Find the indicated term for each geometric series described.

23. $S_n = 1023, a_n = 768, r = 4; a_1$

24. $S_n = 10{,}160, a_n = 5120, r = 2; a_1$

25. $S_n = -1365, n = 12, r = -2; a_1$

26. $S_n = 665, n = 6, r = 1.5; a_1$

27. CONSTRUCTION A pile driver drives a post 27 inches into the ground on its first hit. Each additional hit drives the post $\dfrac{2}{3}$ the distance of the prior hit. Find the total distance the post has been driven after 5 hits.

28. COMMUNICATIONS Hugh Moore e-mails a joke to 5 friends on Sunday morning. Each of these friends e-mails the joke to 5 of her or his friends on Monday morning, and so on. Assuming no duplication, how many people will have heard the joke by the end of Saturday, not including Hugh?

11-5 Practice

Infinite Geometric Series

Find the sum of each infinite geometric series, if it exists.

1. $a_1 = 35, r = \dfrac{2}{7}$ **2.** $a_1 = 26, r = \dfrac{1}{2}$

3. $a_1 = 98, r = -\dfrac{3}{4}$ **4.** $a_1 = 42, r = \dfrac{6}{5}$

5. $a_1 = 112, r = -\dfrac{3}{5}$ **6.** $a_1 = 500, r = \dfrac{1}{5}$

7. $a_1 = 135, r = -\dfrac{1}{2}$ **8.** $18 - 6 + 2 - \ldots$

9. $2 + 6 + 18 + \ldots$ **10.** $6 + 4 + \dfrac{8}{3} + \ldots$

11. $\dfrac{4}{25} + \dfrac{2}{5} + 1 + \ldots$ **12.** $10 + 1 + 0.1 + \ldots$

13. $100 + 20 + 4 + \ldots$ **14.** $-270 + 135 - 67.5 + \ldots$

15. $0.5 + 0.25 + 0.125 + \ldots$ **16.** $\dfrac{7}{10} + \dfrac{7}{100} + \dfrac{7}{1000} + \ldots$

17. $0.8 + 0.08 + 0.008 + \ldots$ **18.** $\dfrac{1}{12} - \dfrac{1}{6} + \dfrac{1}{3} - \ldots$

19. $3 + \dfrac{9}{7} + \dfrac{27}{49} + \ldots$ **20.** $0.3 - 0.003 + 0.00003 - \ldots$

21. $0.06 + 0.006 + 0.0006 + \ldots$ **22.** $\dfrac{2}{3} - 2 + 6 - \ldots$

23. $\displaystyle\sum_{n=1}^{\infty} 3\left(\dfrac{1}{4}\right)^{n-1}$ **24.** $\displaystyle\sum_{n=1}^{\infty} \dfrac{2}{3}\left(-\dfrac{3}{4}\right)^{n-1}$

25. $\displaystyle\sum_{n=1}^{\infty} 18\left(\dfrac{2}{3}\right)^{n-1}$ **26.** $\displaystyle\sum_{n=1}^{\infty} 5(-0.1)^{n-1}$

Write each repeating decimal as a fraction.

27. $0.\overline{6}$ **28.** $0.\overline{09}$ **29.** $0.\overline{43}$ **30.** $0.\overline{27}$

31. $0.\overline{243}$ **32.** $0.\overline{84}$ **33.** $0.\overline{990}$ **34.** $0.\overline{150}$

35. PENDULUMS On its first swing, a pendulum travels 8 feet. On each successive swing, the pendulum travels $\dfrac{4}{5}$ the distance of its previous swing. What is the total distance traveled by the pendulum when it stops swinging?

36. ELASTICITY A ball dropped from a height of 10 feet bounces back $\dfrac{9}{10}$ of that distance. With each successive bounce, the ball continues to reach $\dfrac{9}{10}$ of its previous height. What is the total vertical distance (both up and down) traveled by the ball when it stops bouncing? (*Hint*: Add the total distance the ball falls to the total distance it rises.)

11-6 Practice

Recursion and Special Sequences

Find the first five terms of each sequence.

1. $a_1 = 3, a_{n+1} = a_n + 5$

2. $a_1 = -7, a_{n+1} = a_n + 8$

3. $a_1 = -3, a_{n+1} = 3a_n + 2$

4. $a_1 = -8, a_{n+1} = 10 - a_n$

5. $a_1 = 4, a_{n+1} = n - a_n$

6. $a_1 = -3, a_{n+1} = 3a_n$

7. $a_1 = 4, a_{n+1} = -3a_n + 4$

8. $a_1 = 2, a_{n+1} = -4a_n - 5$

9. $a_1 = 3, a_2 = 1, a_{n+1} = a_n - a_{n-1}$

10. $a_1 = -1, a_2 = 5, a_{n+1} = 4a_{n-1} - a_n$

11. $a_1 = 2, a_2 = -3, a_{n+1} = 5a_n - 8a_{n-1}$

12. $a_1 = -2, a_2 = 1, a_{n+1} = -2a_n + 6a_{n-1}$

Find the first three iterates of each function for the given initial value.

13. $f(x) = 3x + 4, x_0 = -1$

14. $f(x) = 10x + 2, x_0 = -1$

15. $f(x) = 8 + 3x, x_0 = 1$

16. $f(x) = 8 - x, x_0 = -3$

17. $f(x) = 4x + 5, x_0 = -1$

18. $f(x) = 5(x + 3), x_0 = -2$

19. $f(x) = -8x + 9, x_0 = 1$

20. $f(x) = -4x^2, x_0 = -1$

21. $f(x) = x^2 - 1, x_0 = 3$

22. $f(x) = 2x^2; x_0 = 5$

23. INFLATION Iterating the function $c(x) = 1.05x$ gives the future cost of an item at a constant 5% inflation rate. Find the cost of a $2000 ring in five years at 5% inflation.

FRACTALS For Exercises 24–27, use the following information.

Replacing each side of the square shown with the combination of segments below it gives the figure to its right.

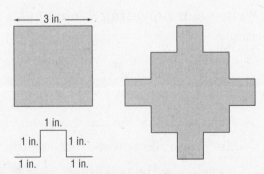

24. What is the perimeter of the original square?

25. What is the perimeter of the new shape?

26. If you repeat the process by replacing each side of the new shape by a proportional combination of 5 segments, what will the perimeter of the third shape be?

27. What function $f(x)$ can you iterate to find the perimeter of each successive shape if you continue this process?

11-7 Practice

The Binomial Theorem

Evaluate each expression.

1. $7!$

2. $11!$

3. $\dfrac{9!}{5!}$

4. $\dfrac{20!}{18!}$

5. $\dfrac{8!}{6!2!}$

6. $\dfrac{8!}{5!3!}$

7. $\dfrac{12!}{6!6!}$

8. $\dfrac{41!}{3!38!}$

Expand each power.

9. $(n + v)^5$

10. $(x - y)^4$

11. $(x + y)^6$

12. $(r + 3)^5$

13. $(m - 5)^5$

14. $(x + 4)^4$

15. $(3x + y)^4$

16. $(2m - y)^4$

17. $(w - 3z)^3$

18. $(2d + 3)^6$

19. $(x + 2y)^5$

20. $(2x - y)^5$

21. $(a - 3b)^4$

22. $(3 - 2z)^4$

23. $(3m - 4n)^3$

24. $(5x - 2y)^4$

Find the indicated term of each expansion.

25. seventh term of $(a + b)^{10}$

26. sixth term of $(m - n)^{10}$

27. ninth term of $(r - s)^{14}$

28. tenth term of $(2x + y)^{12}$

29. fourth term of $(x - 3y)^6$

30. fifth term of $(2x - 1)^9$

31. GEOMETRY How many line segments can be drawn between ten points, no three of which are collinear, if you use exactly two of the ten points to draw each segment?

32. PROBABILITY If you toss a coin 4 times, how many different sequences of tosses will give exactly 3 heads and 1 tail or exactly 1 head and 3 tails?

11-8 Practice

Proof and Mathematical Induction

Prove that each statement is true for all positive integers.

1. $1 + 2 + 4 + 8 + \ldots + 2^{n-1} = 2^n - 1$

2. $1 + 4 + 9 + \ldots + n^2 = \dfrac{n(n+1)(2n+1)}{6}$

3. $18^n - 1$ is a multiple of 17.

Find a counterexample for each statement.

4. $1 + 4 + 7 + \ldots + (3n - 2) = n^3 - n^2 + 1$ **5.** $5^n - 2n - 3$ is divisible by 3.

6. $1 + 3 + 5 + \ldots + (2n - 1) = \dfrac{n^2 + 3n - 2}{2}$ **7.** $1^3 + 2^3 + 3^3 + \ldots + n^3 = n^4 - n^3 + 1$

12-1 Practice

The Counting Principle

State whether the events are *independent* or *dependent*.

1. choosing an ice cream flavor and choosing a topping for the ice cream

2. choosing an offensive player of the game and a defensive player of the game in a professional football game

3. From 15 entries in an art contest, a camp counselor chooses first, second, and third place winners.

4. Jillian is selecting two more courses for her block schedule next semester. She must select one of three morning history classes and one of two afternoon math classes.

Solve each problem.

5. A briefcase lock has 3 rotating cylinders, each containing 10 digits. How many numerical codes are possible?

6. A golf club manufacturer makes irons with 7 different shaft lengths, 3 different grips, 5 different lies, and 2 different club head materials. How many different combinations are offered?

7. There are five different routes that a commuter can take from her home to the office. In how many ways can she make a round trip if she uses a different route coming than going?

8. In how many ways can the four call letters of a radio station be arranged if the first letter must be W or K and no letters repeat?

9. How many 7-digit phone numbers can be formed if the first digit cannot be 0 or 1, and any digit can be repeated?

10. How many 7-digit phone numbers can be formed if the first digit cannot be 0, and any digit can be repeated?

11. How many 7-digit phone numbers can be formed if the first digit cannot be 0 or 1, and if no digit can be repeated?

12. How many 7-digit phone numbers can be formed if the first digit cannot be 0, and if no digit can be repeated?

13. How many 6-character passwords can be formed if the first character is a digit and the remaining 5 characters are letters that can be repeated?

14. How many 6-character passwords can be formed if the first and last characters are digits and the remaining characters are letters? Assume that any character can be repeated.

12-2 Practice

Permutations and Combinations

Evaluate each expression.

1. $P(8, 6)$

2. $P(9, 7)$

3. $P(3, 3)$

4. $P(4, 3)$

5. $P(4, 1)$

6. $P(7, 2)$

7. $C(8, 2)$

8. $C(11, 3)$

9. $C(20, 18)$

10. $C(9, 9)$

11. $C(3, 1)$

12. $C(9, 3) \cdot C(6, 2)$

Determine whether each situation involves a *permutation* or a *combination*. Then find the number of possibilities.

13. selecting a 4-person bobsled team from a group of 9 athletes

14. an arrangement of the letters in the word *Canada*

15. arranging 4 charms on a bracelet that has a clasp, a front, and a back

16. selecting 3 desserts from 10 desserts that are displayed on a dessert cart in a restaurant

17. an arrangement of the letters in the word *annually*

18. forming a 2-person sales team from a group of 12 salespeople

19. making 5-sided polygons by choosing any 5 of 11 points located on a circle to be the vertices

20. seating 5 men and 5 women alternately in a row, beginning with a woman

21. **STUDENT GROUPS** Farmington High is planning its academic festival. All math classes will send 2 representatives to compete in the math bowl. How many different groups of students can be chosen from a class of 16 students?

22. **PHOTOGRAPHY** A photographer is taking pictures of a bride and groom and their 6 attendants. If she takes photographs of 3 people in a group, how many different groups can she photograph?

23. **AIRLINES** An airline is hiring 5 flight attendants. If 8 people apply for the job, how many different groups of 5 attendants can the airline hire?

24. **SUBSCRIPTIONS** A school librarian would like to buy subscriptions to 7 new magazines. Her budget, however, will allow her to buy only 4 new subscriptions. How many different groups of 4 magazines can she choose from the 7 magazines?

12-3 Practice

Probability

A bag contains 1 green, 4 red, and 5 yellow balls. Two balls are selected at random. Find the probability of each selection.

1. P(2 red) **2.** P(1 red and 1 yellow) **3.** P(1 green and 1 yellow)

4. P(2 green) **5.** P(2 red and 1 yellow) **6.** P(1 red and 1 green)

A bank contains 3 pennies, 8 nickels, 4 dimes, and 10 quarters. Two coins are selected at random. Find the probability of each selection.

7. P(2 pennies) **8.** P(2 dimes) **9.** P(1 nickel and 1 dime)

10. P(1 quarter and 1 penny) **11.** P(1 quarter and 1 nickel) **12.** P(2 dimes and 1 quarter)

Henrico visits a home decorating store to choose wallpapers for his new house. The store has 28 books of wallpaper samples, including 10 books of WallPride samples and 18 books of Deluxe Wall Coverings samples. The store will allow Henrico to bring 4 books home for a few days so he can decide which wallpapers he wants to buy. If Henrico randomly chooses 4 books to bring home, find the probability of each selection.

13. P(4 WallPride) **14.** P(2 WallPride and 2 Deluxe)

15. P(1 WallPride and 3 Deluxe) **16.** P(3 WallPride and 1 Deluxe)

For Exercises 17–20, use the table that shows the range of verbal SAT scores for freshmen at a small liberal

Range	400–449	450–499	500–549	550–559	600–649	650+
Number of Students	129	275	438	602	620	412

arts college. If a freshman student is chosen at random, find each probability. Express as decimals rounded to the nearest thousandth.

17. P(400–449) **18.** P(550–559) **19.** P(at least 650)

Find the odds of an event occurring, given the probability of the event.

20. $\frac{4}{11}$ **21.** $\frac{12}{13}$ **22.** $\frac{5}{99}$ **23.** $\frac{1}{1000}$

24. $\frac{5}{16}$ **25.** $\frac{3}{95}$ **26.** $\frac{9}{70}$ **27.** $\frac{8}{15}$

Find the probability of an event occurring, given the odds of the event.

28. 2:23 **29.** 2:5 **30.** 15:1 **31.** 9:7

32. 11:14 **33.** 1000:1 **34.** 12:17 **35.** 8:13

12-4 **Practice**

Multiplying Probabilities

A die is rolled three times. Find each probability.

1. P(three 4s)   **2.** P(no 4s)

3. P(2, then 3, then 1)   **4.** P(three different even numbers)

5. P(any number, then 5, then 5)   **6.** P(even number, then odd number, then 1)

There are 3 nickels, 2 dimes, and 5 quarters in a purse. Three coins are selected in succession at random. Find the probability.

7. P(nickel, then dime, then quarter), if no replacement occurs

8. P(nickel, then dime, then quarter), if replacement occurs

9. P(2 nickels, then 1 quarter), if no replacement occurs

10. P(3 dimes), if replacement occurs

11. P(3 dimes), if no replacement occurs

For Exercises 12 and 13, determine whether the events are *independent* or *dependent*. Then find each probability.

12. Serena is creating a painting. She wants to use 2 more colors. She chooses randomly from 6 shades of red, 10 shades of green, 4 shades of yellow, 4 shades of purple, and 6 shades of blue. What is the probability that she chooses 2 shades of green?

13. Kershel's mother is shopping at a bakery. The owner offers Kershel a cookie from a jar containing 22 chocolate chip cookies, 18 sugar cookies, and 15 oatmeal cookies. Without looking, Kershel selects one, drops it back in, and then randomly selects another. What is the probability that neither selection was a chocolate chip cookie?

14. METEOROLOGY The Fadeeva's are planning a 3-day vacation to the mountains. A long-range forecast reports that the probability of rain each day is 10%. Assuming that the daily probabilities of rain are independent, what is the probability that there is no rain on the first two days, but that it rains on the third day?

RANDOM NUMBERS For Exercises 15 and 16, use the following information.

Anita has a list of 20 jobs around the house to do, and plans to do 3 of them today. She assigns each job a number from 1 to 20, and sets her calculator to generate random numbers from 1 to 20, which can reoccur. Of the jobs, 3 are outside, and the rest are inside.

15. Sketch a tree diagram showing all of the possibilities that the first three numbers generated correspond to inside jobs or outside jobs. Use it to find the probability that the first two numbers correspond to inside jobs, and the third to an outside job.

16. What is the probability that the number generated corresponds to an outside job three times in a row?

12-5 Practice

Adding Probabilities

An urn contains 7 white marbles and 5 blue marbles. Four marbles are selected without replacement. Find each probability.

1. P(4 white or 4 blue)　　　2. P(exactly 3 white)　　　3. P(at least 3 white)

4. P(fewer than 3 white)　　　5. P(3 white or 3 blue)　　　6. P(no white or no blue)

Jason and Maria are playing a board game in which three dice are tossed to determine a player's move. Find each probability.

7. P(two 5s)　　　8. P(three 5s)　　　9. P(at least two 5s)

10. P(no 5s)　　　11. P(one 5)　　　12. P(one 5 or two 5s)

Determine whether the events are *mutually exclusive* or *inclusive*. Then find the probability.

13. A clerk chooses 4 CD players at random for floor displays from a shipment of 24 CD players. If 15 of the players have a blue case and the rest have a red case, what is the probability of choosing 4 players with a blue case or 4 players with a red case?

14. A department store employs 28 high school students, all juniors and seniors. Six of the 12 seniors are females and 12 of the juniors are males. One student employee is chosen at random. What is the probability of selecting a senior or a female?

15. A restaurant has 5 pieces of apple pie, 4 pieces of chocolate cream pie, and 3 pieces of blueberry pie. If Janine selects a piece of pie at random for dessert, what is the probability that she selects either apple or chocolate cream?

16. At a statewide meeting, there are 20 school superintendents, 13 principals, and 6 assistant principals. If one of these people is chosen at random, what is the probability that he or she is either a principal or an assistant principal?

17. An airline has one bank of 13 telephones at a reservations office. Of the 13 operators who work there, 8 take reservations for domestic flights and 5 take reservations for international flights. Seven of the operators taking domestic reservations and 3 of the operators taking international reservations are female. If an operator is chosen at random, what is the probability that the person chosen takes domestic reservations or is a male?

18. **MUSIC** Forty senior citizens were surveyed about their music preferences. The results are displayed in the Venn diagram. If a senior citizen from the survey group is selected at random, what is the probability that he or she likes only country and western music? What is the probability that he or she likes classical and/or country, but not 1940's pop?

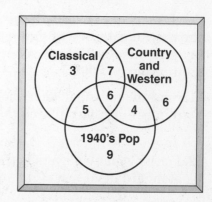

12-6 Practice

Statistical Measures

Find the variance and standard deviation of each set of data to the nearest tenth.

1. {47, 61, 93, 22, 82, 22, 37}

2. {10, 10, 54, 39, 96, 91, 91, 18}

3. {1, 2, 2, 3, 3, 3, 4, 4, 4, 4, 5, 5, 5, 5, 5}

4. {1100, 725, 850, 335, 700, 800, 950}

5. {3.4, 7.1, 8.5, 5.1, 4.7, 6.3, 9.9, 8.4, 3.6}

6. {2.8, 0.5, 1.9, 0.8, 1.9, 1.5, 3.3, 2.6, 0.7, 2.5}

7. HEALTH CARE Eight physicians with 15 patients on a hospital floor see these patients an average of 18 minutes a day. The 22 nurses on the same floor see the patients an average of 3 hours a day. As a hospital administrator, would you quote the mean, median, or mode as an indicator of the amount of daily medical attention the patients on this floor receive? Explain.

For Exercises 8–10, use the frequency table that shows the percent of public school teachers in the U. S. in 1999 who used computers or the Internet at school for various administrative and teaching activities.

Activity	Percent Using Computer or Internet
Create instructional materials	39
Administrative record keeping	34
Communicate with colleagues	23
Gather information for planning lessons	16
Multimedia classroom presentations	8
Access research and best practices for teaching	8
Communicate with parents or students	8
Access model lesson plans	6

Source: National Assessment of Educational Progress

8. Find the mean, median, and mode of the data.

9. Suppose you believe teachers use computers or the Internet too infrequently. Which measure would you quote as the "average?" Explain.

10. Suppose you believe teachers use computers or the Internet too often. Which measure would you quote as the "average?" Explain.

For Exercises 11 and 12, use the frequency table that shows the number of games played by 24 American League baseball players between opening day, 2001 and September 8, 2001.

No. of Games	Frequency
141	4
140	3
139	4
138	5
137	2
136	3
135	3

Source: Major League Baseball

11. Find the mean, median, mode, and standard deviation of the number of games played to the nearest tenth.

12. For how many players is the number of games within one standard deviation of the mean?

12-7 Practice

The Normal Distribution

Determine whether the data in each table appear to be *positively skewed*, *negatively skewed*, or *normally distributed*.

1.

Time Spent at a Museum Exhibit	
Minutes	Frequency
0–25	27
26–50	46
51–75	89
75–100	57
100+	24

2.

Average Age of High School Principals	
Age in Years	Number
31–35	3
36–40	8
41–45	15
46–50	32
51–55	40
56–60	38
60+	4

For Exercises 3 and 4, use the frequency table that shows the number of hours worked per week by 100 high school seniors.

3. Make a histogram of the data.

4. Do the data appear to be *positively skewed*, *negatively skewed*, or *normally distributed*? Explain.

Hours	Number of Students
0–8	30
9–17	45
18–25	20
26+	5

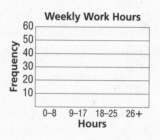

Weekly Work Hours

TESTING For Exercises 5–10, use the following information.

The scores on a test administered to prospective employees are normally distributed with a mean of 100 and a standard deviation of 15.

5. About what percent of the scores are between 70 and 130?

6. About what percent of the scores are between 85 and 130?

7. About what percent of the scores are over 115?

8. About what percent of the scores are lower than 85 or higher than 115?

9. If 80 people take the test, how many would you expect to score higher than 130?

10. If 75 people take the test, how many would you expect to score lower than 85?

11. TEMPERATURE The daily July surface temperature of a lake at a resort has a mean of 82° and a standard deviation of 4.2°. If you prefer to swim when the temperature is at least 77.8°, about what percent of the days does the temperature meet your preference?

12-8 **Practice**

Binomial Experiments

Find each probability if a coin is tossed 6 times.

1. P(exactly 3 tails)   **2.** P(exactly 5 tails)

3. P(0 tails)   **4.** P(at least 4 heads)

5. P(at least 4 tails)   **6.** P(at most 2 tails)

The probability of Chris making a free throw is $\frac{2}{3}$. If she shoots 5 times, find each probability.

7. P(all missed)   **8.** P(all made)

9. P(exactly 2 made)   **10.** P(exactly 1 missed)

11. P(at least 3 made)   **12.** P(at most 2 made)

When Tarin and Sam play a certain board game, the probability that Tarin will win a game is $\frac{3}{4}$. If they play 5 games, find each probability.

13. P(Sam wins only once)   **14.** P(Tarin wins exactly twice)

15. P(Sam wins exactly 3 games)   **16.** P(Sam wins at least 1 game)

17. P(Tarin wins at least 3 games)   **18.** P(Tarin wins at most 2 games)

19. SAFETY In August 2001, the American Automobile Association reported that 73% of Americans use seat belts. In a random selection of 10 Americans in 2001, what is the probability that exactly half of them use seat belts? **Source:** AAA

HEALTH For Exercises 20 and 21, use the following information.

In 2001, the American Heart Association reported that 50 percent of the Americans who receive heart transplants are ages 50–64 and 20 percent are ages 35–49. **Source:** American Heart Association

20. In a randomly selected group of 10 heart transplant recipients, what is the probability that at least 8 of them are ages 50–64?

21. In a randomly selected group of 5 heart transplant recipients, what is the probability that 2 of them are ages 35–49?

12-9 Practice

Sampling and Error

Determine whether each situation would produce a random sample. Write *yes* or *no* and explain your answer.

1. calling every twentieth registered voter to determine whether people own or rent their homes in your community

2. predicting local election results by polling people in every twentieth residence in all the different neighborhoods of your community

3. to find out why not many students are using the library, a school's librarian gives a questionnaire to every tenth student entering the library

4. testing overall performance of tires on interstate highways only

5. selecting every 50th hamburger from a fast-food restaurant chain and determining its fat content to assess the fat content of hamburgers served in fast-food restaurant chains throughout the country

6. assigning all shift workers in a manufacturing plant a unique identification number, and then placing the numbers in a hat and drawing 30 at random to determine the annual average salary of the workers

Find the margin of sampling error to the nearest percent.

7. $p = 26\%, n = 100$

8. $p = 55\%, n = 100$

9. $p = 75\%, n = 500$

10. $p = 14\%, n = 500$

11. $p = 96\%, n = 1000$

12. $p = 21\%, n = 1000$

13. $p = 34\%, n = 1000$

14. $p = 49\%, n = 1500$

15. $p = 65\%, n = 1500$

16. **COMPUTING** According to a poll of 500 teenagers, 43% said that they use a personal computer at home. What is the margin of sampling error?

17. **TRUST** A survey of 605 people, ages 13–33, shows that 68% trust their parents more than their best friends to tell them the truth. What is the margin of sampling error?

18. **PRODUCTIVITY** A study by the University of Illinois in 1995 showed an increase in productivity by 10% of the employees who wore headsets and listened to music of their choice while they were working. The margin of sampling error for the study was about 7%. How many employees participated in the study?

13-1 Practice

Right Triangle Trigonometry

Find the values of the six trigonometric functions for angle θ.

1.

2.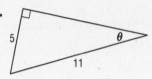

3.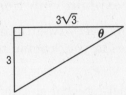

Write an equation involving sin, cos, or tan that can be used to find x. Then solve the equation. Round measures of sides to the nearest tenth and measures of angles to the nearest degree.

4.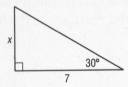

5.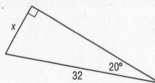

6.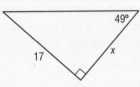

7.

8.

9.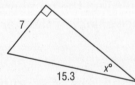

Solve $\triangle ABC$ by using the given measurements. Round measures of sides to the nearest tenth and measures of angles to the nearest degree.

10. $A = 35°, a = 12$

11. $B = 71°, b = 25$

12. $B = 36°, c = 8$

13. $a = 4, b = 7$

14. $A = 17°, c = 3.2$

15. $b = 52, c = 95$

16. **SURVEYING** John stands 150 meters from a water tower and sights the top at an angle of elevation of 36°. How tall is the tower? Round to the nearest meter.

13-2 Practice

Angles and Angle Measure

Draw an angle with the given measure in standard position.

1. 210°

2. 305°

3. 580°

4. 135°

5. −450°

6. −560°

Rewrite each degree measure in radians and each radian measure in degrees.

7. 18°   **8.** 6°   **9.** 870°   **10.** 347°

11. −72°   **12.** −820°   **13.** −250°   **14.** −165°

15. 4π **16.** $\dfrac{5\pi}{2}$ **17.** $\dfrac{13\pi}{5}$ **18.** $\dfrac{13\pi}{30}$

19. $-\dfrac{9\pi}{2}$ **20.** $-\dfrac{7\pi}{12}$ **21.** $-\dfrac{3\pi}{8}$ **22.** $-\dfrac{3\pi}{16}$

Find one angle with positive measure and one angle with negative measure coterminal with each angle.

23. 65°   **24.** 80°   **25.** 285°

26. 110°   **27.** −37°   **28.** −93°

29. $\dfrac{2\pi}{5}$ **30.** $\dfrac{5\pi}{6}$ **31.** $\dfrac{17\pi}{6}$

32. $-\dfrac{3\pi}{2}$ **33.** $-\dfrac{\pi}{4}$ **34.** $-\dfrac{5\pi}{12}$

35. TIME Find both the degree and radian measures of the angle through which the hour hand on a clock rotates from 5 A.M. to 10 A.M.

36. ROTATION A truck with 16-inch radius wheels is driven at 77 feet per second (52.5 miles per hour). Find the measure of the angle through which a point on the outside of the wheel travels each second. Round to the nearest degree and nearest radian.

13-3 Practice

Trigonometric Functions of General Angles

Find the exact values of the six trigonometric functions of θ if the terminal side of θ in standard position contains the given point.

1. $(6, 8)$

2. $(-20, 21)$

3. $(-2, -5)$

Find the reference angle for the angle with the given measure.

4. $236°$

5. $\dfrac{13\pi}{8}$

6. $-210°$

7. $-\dfrac{7\pi}{4}$

Find the exact value of each trigonometric function.

8. $\tan 135°$

9. $\cot 210°$

10. $\cot(-90°)$

11. $\cos 405°$

12. $\tan \dfrac{5\pi}{3}$

13. $\csc\left(-\dfrac{3\pi}{4}\right)$

14. $\cot 2\pi$

15. $\tan \dfrac{13\pi}{6}$

Suppose θ is an angle in standard position whose terminal side is in the given quadrant. For each function, find the exact values of the remaining five trigonometric functions of θ.

16. $\tan \theta = -\dfrac{12}{5}$, Quadrant IV

17. $\sin \theta = \dfrac{2}{3}$, Quadrant III

18. LIGHT Light rays that "bounce off" a surface are *reflected* by the surface. If the surface is partially transparent, some of the light rays are bent or *refracted* as they pass from the air through the material. The angles of reflection θ_1 and of refraction θ_2 in the diagram at the right are related by the equation $\sin \theta_1 = n \sin \theta_2$. If $\theta_1 = 60°$ and $n = \sqrt{3}$, find the measure of θ_2.

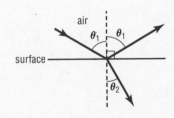

19. FORCE A cable running from the top of a utility pole to the ground exerts a horizontal pull of 800 Newtons and a vertical pull of $800\sqrt{3}$ Newtons. What is the sine of the angle θ between the cable and the ground? What is the measure of this angle?

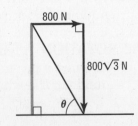

Glencoe Algebra 2

13-4 Practice

Law of Sines

Find the area of △ABC to the nearest tenth.

1.
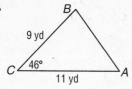

9 yd
46°
11 yd

2.

12 m 58°
15 m

3.
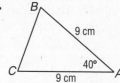

9 cm
40°
9 cm

4. $C = 32°$, $a = 12.6$ m, $b = 8.9$ m

5. $B = 27°$, $a = 14.9$ cm, $c = 18.6$ cm

6. $A = 17.4°$, $b = 12$ km, $c = 14$ km

7. $A = 34°$, $b = 19.4$ ft, $c = 8.6$ ft

Solve each triangle. Round measures of sides to the nearest tenth and measures of angles to the nearest degree.

8. $A = 50°$, $B = 30°$, $c = 9$

9. $A = 56°$, $B = 38°$, $a = 12$

10. $A = 80°$, $C = 14°$, $a = 40$

11. $B = 47°$, $C = 112°$, $b = 13$

12. $A = 72°$, $a = 8$, $c = 6$

13. $A = 25°$, $C = 107°$, $b = 12$

Determine whether each triangle has *no* solution, *one* solution, or *two* solutions. Then solve each triangle. Round measures of sides to the nearest tenth and measures of angles to the nearest degree.

14. $A = 29°$, $a = 6$, $b = 13$

15. $A = 70°$, $a = 25$, $b = 20$

16. $A = 113°$, $a = 21$, $b = 25$

17. $A = 110°$, $a = 20$, $b = 8$

18. $A = 66°$, $a = 12$, $b = 7$

19. $A = 54°$, $a = 5$, $b = 8$

20. $A = 45°$, $a = 15$, $b = 18$

21. $A = 60°$, $a = 4\sqrt{3}$, $b = 8$

22. **WILDLIFE** Sarah Phillips, an officer for the Department of Fisheries and Wildlife, checks boaters on a lake to make sure they do not disturb two osprey nesting sites. She leaves a dock and heads due north in her boat to the first nesting site. From here, she turns 5° north of due west and travels an additional 2.14 miles to the second nesting site. She then travels 6.7 miles directly back to the dock. How far from the dock is the first osprey nesting site? Round to the nearest tenth.

13-5 Practice

Law of Cosines

Determine whether each triangle should be solved by beginning with the Law of Sines or Law of Cosines. Then solve each triangle. Round measures of sides to the nearest tenth and measures of angles to the nearest degree.

1.

2.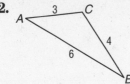

3.

4. $a = 16, b = 20, C = 54°$

5. $B = 71°, c = 6, a = 11$

6. $A = 37°, a = 20, b = 18$

7. $C = 35°, a = 18, b = 24$

8. $a = 8, b = 6, c = 9$

9. $A = 23°, b = 10, c = 12$

10. $a = 4, b = 5, c = 8$

11. $B = 46.6°, C = 112°, b = 13$

12. $A = 46.3°, a = 35, b = 30$

13. $a = 16.4, b = 21.1, c = 18.5$

14. $C = 43.5°, b = 8, c = 6$

15. $A = 78.3°, b = 7, c = 11$

16. **SATELLITES** Two radar stations 2.4 miles apart are tracking an airplane. The straight-line distance between Station A and the plane is 7.4 miles. The straight-line distance between Station B and the plane is 6.9 miles. What is the angle of elevation from Station A to the plane? Round to the nearest degree.

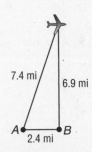

17. **DRAFTING** Marion is using a computer-aided drafting program to produce a drawing for a client. She begins a triangle by drawing a segment 4.2 inches long from point A to point B. From B, she moves 42° degrees counterclockwise from the segment connecting A and B and draws a second segment that is 6.4 inches long, ending at point C. To the nearest tenth, how long is the segment from C to A?

13-6 Practice

Circular Functions

The given point *P* is located on the unit circle. Find sin θ and cos θ.

1. $P\left(-\dfrac{1}{2}, \dfrac{\sqrt{3}}{2}\right)$

2. $P\left(\dfrac{20}{29}, -\dfrac{21}{29}\right)$

3. $P(0.8, 0.6)$

4. $P(0, -1)$

5. $P\left(-\dfrac{\sqrt{2}}{2}, -\dfrac{\sqrt{2}}{2}\right)$

6. $P\left(\dfrac{\sqrt{3}}{2}, \dfrac{1}{2}\right)$

Find the exact value of each function.

7. $\cos \dfrac{7\pi}{4}$

8. $\sin(-30°)$

9. $\sin\left(-\dfrac{2\pi}{3}\right)$

10. $\cos(-330°)$

11. $\cos 600°$

12. $\sin \dfrac{9\pi}{2}$

13. $\cos 7\pi$

14. $\cos\left(-\dfrac{11\pi}{4}\right)$

15. $\sin(-225°)$

16. $\sin 585°$

17. $\cos\left(-\dfrac{10\pi}{3}\right)$

18. $\sin 840°$

Determine the period of each function.

19.

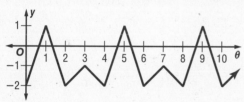

20.

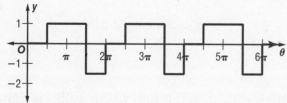

21. FERRIS WHEELS A Ferris wheel with a diameter of 100 feet completes 2.5 revolutions per minute. What is the period of the function that describes the height of a seat on the outside edge of the Ferris Wheel as a function of time?

13-7 Practice

Inverse Trigonometric Functions

Write each equation in the form of an inverse function.

1. $\beta = \cos \alpha$

2. $\tan \beta = \alpha$

3. $y = \tan 120°$

4. $-\dfrac{1}{2} = \cos x$

5. $\sin \dfrac{2\pi}{3} = \dfrac{\sqrt{3}}{2}$

6. $\cos \dfrac{\pi}{3} = \dfrac{1}{2}$

Solve each equation by finding the value of x to the nearest degree.

7. $\text{Arcsin } 1 = x$

8. $\text{Cos}^{-1} \dfrac{\sqrt{3}}{2} = x$

9. $x = \tan^{-1}\left(-\dfrac{\sqrt{3}}{3}\right)$

10. $x = \text{Arccos } \dfrac{\sqrt{2}}{2}$

11. $x = \text{Arctan }(-\sqrt{3})$

12. $\text{Sin}^{-1}\left(-\dfrac{1}{2}\right) = x$

Find each value. Write angle measures in radians. Round to the nearest hundredth.

13. $\text{Cos}^{-1}\left(-\dfrac{\sqrt{3}}{2}\right)$

14. $\text{Sin}^{-1}\left(-\dfrac{\sqrt{2}}{2}\right)$

15. $\text{Arctan }\left(-\dfrac{\sqrt{3}}{3}\right)$

16. $\tan\left(\text{Cos}^{-1} \dfrac{1}{2}\right)$

17. $\cos\left[\text{Sin}^{-1}\left(-\dfrac{3}{5}\right)\right]$

18. $\cos\left[\text{Arctan }(-1)\right]$

19. $\tan\left(\sin^{-1} \dfrac{12}{13}\right)$

20. $\sin\left(\text{Arctan } \dfrac{\sqrt{3}}{3}\right)$

21. $\text{Cos}^{-1}\left(\tan \dfrac{3\pi}{4}\right)$

22. $\text{Sin}^{-1}\left(\cos \dfrac{\pi}{3}\right)$

23. $\sin\left(2 \text{ Cos}^{-1} \dfrac{15}{17}\right)$

24. $\cos\left(2 \text{ Sin}^{-1} \dfrac{\sqrt{3}}{2}\right)$

25. PULLEYS The equation $x = \cos^{-1} 0.95$ describes the angle through which pulley A moves, and $y = \cos^{-1} 0.17$ describes the angle through which pulley B moves. Both angles are greater than 270° and less than 360°. Which pulley moves through a greater angle?

26. FLYWHEELS The equation $y = \text{Arctan } 1$ describes the counterclockwise angle through which a flywheel rotates in 1 millisecond. Through how many degrees has the flywheel rotated after 25 milliseconds?

14-1 Practice

Graphing Trigonometric Functions

Find the amplitude, if it exists, and period of each function. Then graph each function.

1. $y = -4 \sin \theta$

2. $y = \cot \frac{1}{2}\theta$

3. $y = \cos 5\theta$

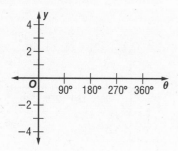

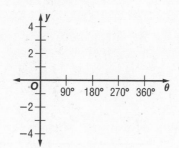

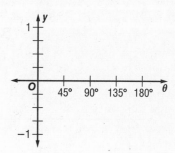

4. $y = \csc \frac{3}{4}\theta$

5. $y = 2 \tan \frac{1}{2}\theta$

6. $2y = \sin \theta$

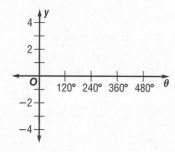

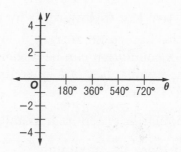

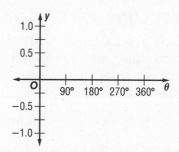

FORCE **For Exercises 7 and 8, use the following information.**

An anchoring cable exerts a force of 500 Newtons on a pole. The force has the horizontal and vertical components F_x and F_y. (A force of one Newton (N), is the force that gives an acceleration of 1 m/sec² to a mass of 1 kg.)

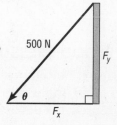

7. The function $F_x = 500 \cos \theta$ describes the relationship between the angle θ and the horizontal force. What are the amplitude and period of this function?

8. The function $F_y = 500 \sin \theta$ describes the relationship between the angle θ and the vertical force. What are the amplitude and period of this function?

WEATHER **For Exercises 9 and 10, use the following information.**

The function $y = 60 + 25 \sin \frac{\pi}{6}t$, where t is in months and $t = 0$ corresponds to April 15, models the average high temperature in degrees Fahrenheit in Centerville.

9. Determine the period of this function. What does this period represent?

10. What is the maximum high temperature and when does this occur?

14-2 Practice

Translations of Trigonometric Graphs

State the vertical shift, amplitude, period, and phase shift for each function. Then graph the function.

1. $y = \dfrac{1}{2} \tan\left(\theta - \dfrac{\pi}{2}\right)$ 　　　 **2.** $y = 2\cos(\theta + 30°) + 3$ 　　　 **3.** $y = 3\csc(2\theta + 60°) - 2.5$

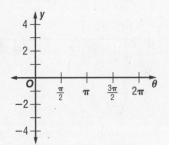 　 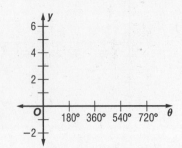 　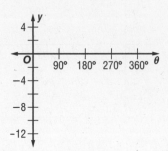

ECOLOGY For Exercises 4–6, use the following information.

The population of an insect species in a stand of trees follows the growth cycle of a particular tree species. The insect population can be modeled by the function $y = 40 + 30 \sin 6t$, where t is the number of years since the stand was first cut in November, 1920.

4. How often does the insect population reach its maximum level?

5. When did the population last reach its maximum?

6. What condition in the stand do you think corresponds with a minimum insect population?

BLOOD PRESSURE For Exercises 7–9, use the following information.

Jason's blood pressure is 110 over 70, meaning that the pressure oscillates between a maximum of 110 and a minimum of 70. Jason's heart rate is 45 beats per minute. The function that represents Jason's blood pressure P can be modeled using a sine function with no phase shift.

7. Find the amplitude, midline, and period in seconds of the function.

8. Write a function that represents Jason's blood pressure P after t seconds.

9. Graph the function.

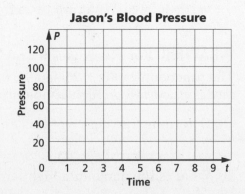

14-3 Practice

Trigonometric Identities

Find the value of each expression.

1. $\sin \theta$, if $\cos \theta = \dfrac{5}{13}$ and $0° \le \theta < 90°$

2. $\sec \theta$, if $\sin \theta = -\dfrac{15}{17}$ and $180° < \theta < 270°$

3. $\cot \theta$, if $\cos \theta = \dfrac{3}{10}$ and $270° < \theta < 360°$

4. $\sin \theta$, if $\cot \theta = \dfrac{1}{2}$ and $0° \le \theta < 90°$

5. $\cot \theta$, if $\csc \theta = -\dfrac{3}{2}$ and $180° < \theta < 270°$

6. $\sec \theta$, if $\csc \theta = -8$ and $270° < \theta < 360°$

7. $\sec \theta$, if $\tan \theta = 4$ and $180° < \theta < 270°$

8. $\sin \theta$, if $\tan \theta = -\dfrac{1}{2}$ and $270° < \theta < 360°$

9. $\cot \theta$, if $\tan \theta = \dfrac{2}{5}$ and $0° \le \theta < 90°$

10. $\cot \theta$, if $\cos \theta = \dfrac{1}{3}$ and $270° < \theta < 360°$

Simplify each expression.

11. $\csc \theta \tan \theta$

12. $\dfrac{\sin^2 \theta}{\tan^2 \theta}$

13. $\sin^2 \theta \cot^2 \theta$

14. $\cot^2 \theta + 1$

15. $\dfrac{\csc^2 \theta - \cot^2 \theta}{1 - \cos^2 \theta}$

16. $\dfrac{\csc \theta - \sin \theta}{\cos \theta}$

17. $\sin \theta + \cos \theta \cot \theta$

18. $\dfrac{\cos \theta}{1 - \sin \theta} - \dfrac{\cos \theta}{1 + \sin \theta}$

19. $\sec^2 \theta \cos^2 \theta - \tan^2 \theta$

20. AERIAL PHOTOGRAPHY The illustration shows a plane taking an aerial photograph of point A. Because the point is directly below the plane, there is no distortion in the image. For any point B not directly below the plane, however, the increase in distance creates distortion in the photograph. This is because as the distance from the camera to the point being photographed increases, the exposure of the film reduces by $(\sin \theta)(\csc \theta - \sin \theta)$. Express $(\sin \theta)(\csc \theta - \sin \theta)$ in terms of $\cos \theta$ only.

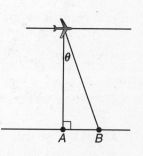

21. TSUNAMIS The equation $y = a \sin \theta t$ represents the height of the waves passing a buoy at a time t in seconds. Express a in terms of $\csc \theta t$.

14-4 Practice

Verifying Trigonometric Identities

Verify that each of the following is an identity.

1. $\dfrac{\sin^2 \theta + \cos^2 \theta}{\cos^2 \theta} = \sec^2 \theta$

2. $\dfrac{\cos^2 \theta}{1 - \sin^2 \theta} = 1$

3. $(1 + \sin \theta)(1 - \sin \theta) = \cos^2 \theta$

4. $\tan^4 \theta + 2 \tan^2 \theta + 1 = \sec^4 \theta$

5. $\cos^2 \theta \cot^2 \theta = \cot^2 \theta - \cos^2 \theta$

6. $(\sin^2 \theta)(\csc^2 \theta + \sec^2 \theta) = \sec^2 \theta$

7. PROJECTILES The square of the initial velocity of an object launched from the ground is $v^2 = \dfrac{2gh}{\sin^2 \theta}$, where θ is the angle between the ground and the initial path, h is the maximum height reached, and g is the acceleration due to gravity. Verify the identity $\dfrac{2gh}{\sin^2 \theta} = \dfrac{2gh \sec^2 \theta}{\sec^2 \theta - 1}$.

8. LIGHT The intensity of a light source measured in candles is given by $I = ER^2 \sec \theta$, where E is the illuminance in foot candles on a surface, R is the distance in feet from the light source, and θ is the angle between the light beam and a line perpendicular to the surface. Verify the identity $ER^2(1 + \tan^2 \theta) \cos \theta = ER^2 \sec \theta$.

14-5 Practice

Sum and Difference of Angles Formulas

Find the exact value of each expression.

1. $\cos 75°$

2. $\cos 375°$

3. $\sin (-165°)$

4. $\sin (-105°)$

5. $\sin 150°$

6. $\cos 240°$

7. $\sin 225°$

8. $\sin (-75°)$

9. $\sin 195°$

Verify that each of the following is an identity.

10. $\cos (180° - \theta) = -\cos \theta$

11. $\sin (360° + \theta) = \sin \theta$

12. $\sin (45° + \theta) - \sin (45° - \theta) = \sqrt{2} \sin \theta$

13. $\cos \left(x - \dfrac{\pi}{6}\right) + \sin \left(x - \dfrac{\pi}{3}\right) = \sin x$

14. SOLAR ENERGY On March 21, the maximum amount of solar energy that falls on a square foot of ground at a certain location is given by $E \sin (90° - \phi)$, where ϕ is the latitude of the location and E is a constant. Use the difference of angles formula to find the amount of solar energy, in terms of $\cos \phi$, for a location that has a latitude of ϕ.

ELECTRICITY In Exercises 15 and 16, use the following information.

In a certain circuit carrying alternating current, the formula $i = 2 \sin (120t)$ can be used to find the current i in amperes after t seconds.

15. Rewrite the formula using the sum of two angles.

16. Use the sum of angles formula to find the exact current at $t = 1$ second.

14-6 Practice

Double-Angle and Half-Angle Formulas

Find the exact values of $\sin 2\theta$, $\cos 2\theta$, $\sin \frac{\theta}{2}$, and $\cos \frac{\theta}{2}$ for each of the following.

1. $\cos \theta = \frac{5}{13}$, $0° < \theta < 90°$

2. $\sin \theta = \frac{8}{17}$, $90° < \theta < 180°$

3. $\cos \theta = \frac{1}{4}$, $270° < \theta < 360°$

4. $\sin \theta = -\frac{2}{3}$, $180° < \theta < 270°$

Find the exact value of each expression by using the half-angle formulas.

5. $\tan 105°$ **6.** $\tan 15°$ **7.** $\cos 67.5°$ **8.** $\sin \left(-\frac{\pi}{8}\right)$

Verify that each of the following is an identity.

9. $\sin^2 \frac{\theta}{2} = \dfrac{\tan \theta - \sin \theta}{2 \tan \theta}$

10. $\sin 4\theta = 4 \cos 2\theta \sin \theta \cos \theta$

11. AERIAL PHOTOGRAPHY In aerial photography, there is a reduction in film exposure for any point X not directly below the camera. The reduction E_θ is given by $E_\theta = E_0 \cos^4 \theta$, where θ is the angle between the perpendicular line from the camera to the ground and the line from the camera to point X, and E_0 is the exposure for the point directly below the camera. Using the identity $2 \sin^2 \theta = 1 - \cos 2\theta$, verify that $E_0 \cos^4 \theta = E_0 \left(\frac{1}{2} + \frac{\cos 2\theta}{2}\right)^2$.

12. IMAGING A scanner takes thermal images from altitudes of 300 to 12,000 meters. The width W of the swath covered by the image is given by $W = 2H' \tan \theta$, where H' is the height and θ is half the scanner's field of view. Verify that $\dfrac{2H' \sin 2\theta}{1 + \cos 2\theta} = 2H' \tan \theta$.

14-7 Practice

Solving Trigonometric Equations

Find all solutions of each equation for the given interval.

1. $\sin 2\theta = \cos \theta$, $90° \leq \theta < 180°$

2. $\sqrt{2} \cos \theta = \sin 2\theta$, $0° \leq \theta < 360°$

3. $\cos 4\theta = \cos 2\theta$, $180° \leq \theta < 360°$

4. $\cos \theta + \cos (90 - \theta) = 0$, $0 \leq \theta < 2\pi$

5. $2 + \cos \theta = 2 \sin^2 \theta$, $\pi \leq \theta \leq \dfrac{3\pi}{2}$

6. $\tan^2 \theta + \sec \theta = 1$, $\dfrac{\pi}{2} \leq \theta < \pi$

Solve each equation for all values of θ if θ is measured in radians.

7. $\cos^2 \theta = \sin^2 \theta$

8. $\cot \theta = \cot^3 \theta$

9. $\sqrt{2} \sin^3 \theta = \sin^2 \theta$

10. $\cos^2 \theta \sin \theta = \sin \theta$

11. $2 \cos 2\theta = 1 - 2 \sin^2 \theta$

12. $\sec^2 \theta = 2$

Solve each equation for all values of θ if θ is measured in degrees.

13. $\sin^2 \theta \cos \theta = \cos \theta$

14. $\csc^2 \theta - 3 \csc \theta + 2 = 0$

15. $\dfrac{3}{1 + \cos \theta} = 4(1 - \cos \theta)$

16. $\sqrt{2} \cos^2 \theta = \cos^2 \theta$

Solve each equation for all values of θ.

17. $4 \sin^2 \theta = 3$

18. $4 \sin^2 \theta - 1 = 0$

19. $2 \sin^2 \theta - 3 \sin \theta = -1$

20. $\cos 2\theta + \sin \theta - 1 = 0$

21. WAVES Waves are causing a buoy to float in a regular pattern in the water. The vertical position of the buoy can be described by the equation $h = 2 \sin x$. Write an expression that describes the position of the buoy when its height is at its midline.

22. ELECTRICITY The electric current in a certain circuit with an alternating current can be described by the formula $i = 3 \sin 240t$, where i is the current in amperes and t is the time in seconds. Write an expression that describes the times at which there is no current.

Visit us online at:

www.algebra2.com

A Division of The McGraw-Hill Companies

ISBN 0-07-828024-9

9 780078 280245

90000

McGraw Hill **Glencoe
McGraw-Hill**

T3-AAI-1